For P[...]

handwritten: For P...

Echoes of Another Time

Hazel McIntyre

handwritten: Best wishes

handwritten signature: Hazel McIntyre

Moran Publications

First Published in Ireland by
Moran Publications
October 2000

ISBN 0-9524426-6-3

Typset: Stuart Clarke
Proof Reading: Denise Cavanagh
Cover Design: Martina McFadden
Illustrations: Jean McGuinness

Printed and bound in Ireland by:
Browne Printing, Letterkenny, Co Donegal

I would like to thank my family and friends for their support and encouragement particularly my husband Charles, Stuart, Robert, Colleen, wee Darragh, Denise Cavanagh, Michelle Mc Cole, Frank Galligan and all my goods friends in Inishowen and Derry.

Contents

Winter Dance 13

Smuggling 21

Waltzing, Green Apples and Woodbine 26

Dark Recollections 32

Late Home 37

The Visit 45

Katie's Tales 54

Fear was the Weapon 58

A City Man's Gifts 62

Christmas Shoppers 68

Wedding Fever 72

Easy Money in a Modern World 85

Contents

The Confirmation Class 89

The Homecoming 94

Presbyterian Cow 105

The Patent Shoes 109

Satin Frocks and Missions 116

Summer Rain and Jimmy Shand 121

In Memory of an Animal Lover 126

Echoes 131

Boots for Christmas 139

A Police Record 146

The Funeral 153

To go at Christmas 157

Introduction

When Thomas Ó Crohan started writing his famous
book 'The Islanders' about growing up on the
Great Blaskets, he described it as an attempt "to set
down the character of the people about me." Hazel
McIntyre also writes about those around her in this,
her fourth publication. Although the setting is
different, the Inishowen peninsula, her focus is on
the middle years of the last century. She uses the
storyteller's technique to perfection, developing
scenes and recreating memories from her childhood
growing up in an idyllic world in North Donegal.
With the clever use of anecdote and dialogue, she
envelopes the reader in its joys and wonders, fears
and contradictions. Her sense of community is
strongly evoked and images flow from her pen to
capture the beauty of an innocent and almost
mythical time, with humour and empathy. At the
same time, she explores with great sensitivity, the

fears and emotions that are present in the lives of her characters, as they try to interpret with humour and grace, the everyday events that are part of the daily round. Her inspiration comes from the manner in which her characters react to these happenings. The reader is reminded of the values of the time, and suddenly realises just how much has changed in this technological age. Another writer who loved this peninsula intensely was Joyce Cary, who recalled how one of his books came into being. He was referring to 'A House of Children,' which he described as "recollections suddenly called up." Hazel McIntyre has treated us to more that a feast of recollection: her skill as a storyteller has reopened for the reader a world that has indeed passed by too quickly.

Seán Beattie
Writer and Historian

WINTER AT KINNAGOE BAY

Crystal drops of ice,
Formed on drooping hawthorn branches,
Catch early morning rays,
And glisten incandescent brightness.

Icy ponds of water,
Reflect the world in winter splendour,
As the gushing frigid river,
Pours towards the sea with fervour.

Small birds alight from trees,
And peck the frosted ground,
Searching through the snow,
For food which must be found.

White foaming rivers,
Snake up the golden sands,
And heather covered cliffs,
Sweep down from high headlands.

Standing rocks rise upwards,
And reach towards the sky,
Strange shapes, wondrous forms,
Above which, seagulls cry.

Humble thatched ruins,
Reminders of a bygone day,
Sit on snow peppered hills,
Keeping silent watch over Kinnagoe Bay.

Denise Cavanagh

Winter Dance

They silently sifted through the treasures and secrets of their mother's old wooden trunk box. Hours passed, quickly lost in unashamed nostalgia - gazing at old photographs, reading old letters, marvelling at the foresight of preserving these snippets of past memories from another time. At the bottom, a furry object made Hanna recoil in fearful anticipation. As the old fur wrap emerged from its hiding place, the head and tail of the animal that once inhabited the fur still attached and as she stared at the beady glass eyes, departed memory of a long ago winter night awoke.

The posters advertising the big dance at Borderland stared out from shop windows and lamp-posts for miles around. To Hanna this event was not to be missed at any cost. But, it needed planning well in advance and she had just two weeks to do it.
After school on cold, wintry evenings she would cycle miles to the scattered homes of the teenagers in the neighbourhood to try to encourage enough passengers to make the fifteen-mile journey to the dance.
"I need at least six passengers to make the journey worthwhile," the mini-bus driver had said.

Now, as she stood in front of the bedroom mirror admiring her red taffeta outfit and black patent stilettos, Hanna felt a mounting excitement at the thought of the night ahead.
In the kitchen her father glanced at her from the side of the newspaper.
"You're not surely going out dressed in that flimsy get-up on a bitter night like this?" he said, with disapproval. "And the forecast is bad too."
"It'll be warm in the bus."
"You're not leaving this house without a warm

coat." Her mother's stern voice coming from behind startled her, making her jump. Turning around she saw her old brown school coat over her arm. With sinking spirits she put it on and immediately felt like a drab schoolgirl again. When the bus arrived, Hanna bid her parents a cheery farewell, and then in the hallway she removed the brown coat and threw it over the hallstand.

She regretted her hasty decision to discard the coat almost immediately, when her teeth began to chatter in the cold, draughty bus and she longed to huddle inside its familiar warmth.

About two miles into the journey the first snowflakes began to fall. Soon the snow began to come down thick and fast, driven by a strong north-east wind. The bus slowed down to a crawl and the now silent passengers peered warily at the few feet of visibility ahead.

A mile or so on, the driver pulled up. "Look, we're not going to make it to Borderland. But, I have an idea. There is a wee dance up the road in Connelly's barn. We could make it that far." There was a minute's disappointed silence as we stared at the flying snow lighted up by the headlights.

"I suppose that will have to do," a voice sounded from the blackness.

Echoes of Another Time

The sounds of a melodeon greeted them, as they made their way up the stone steps of the barn. They paid their entrance fee and went in.

There were no more than half a dozen people inside. The naked bulbs swayed in the draughts from the windows causing the light to tremble, and tall shadows flickered back and forth against the walls.

For Hanna, the joy of anticipation for the dance she had dreamed about for weeks was gone, as she stood shivering in her flimsy taffeta frock.

A short man in Wellington boots ambled across the floor close to where they were standing.

Removing the lid from the can he was carrying, he poured some of the liquid over the smouldering turf fire. "Stand back," he shouted. Then from a safe distance, he lit a match and threw it at the fire.

A loud boom…and the flames leapt outwards and upwards. We moved back to our former position, our faces taking on the red glow of warmth.

A drummer and an accordion player soon joined the melodeon player.

"Ladies and gentlemen," the drummer's voice sounded over the microphone, "It's a raw, cold night. Now take your partners for a military two-step. Come on now, let's see you all on the floor."

Hanna had imagined herself jiving in Borderland in her red taffeta and patent stilettos and now here she was, dancing a military two step, with a man in

Wellington boots.

By the end of the second dance the barn was full and everybody danced, the snow and cold of the night forgotten.

He stood at the doorway dressed in a navy overcoat and rubber boots with two bulky objects peering out of the coat pockets. She watched him remove the boots and replace them with the shoes he took out of the overcoat pockets. When he had removed the big coat, in Hanna's eyes he looked like her favourite rock heart-throb. Suddenly, he glanced in her direction and as their eyes met, he flashed a radiant smile at her, then he strode across the floor and asked her to dance. His name was Mike and Hanna was suddenly glad of the snow-storm that brought her here.

"We went to Borderland first," he said, "but the dance was cancelled.

The band got stuck in the snow-storm. We decided to head for here and then our car got stuck," he told Hanna, as they waltzed around the rutted barn floor.

During the last dance Mike offered to walk her to the bus. "Where's your coat?" he asked, as he put on the big overcoat again. "I left it at home.

Thought it would be warm enough in the bus," she explained.

"You'll freeze outside. It's snowing like mad and the wind would cut you in two. Here, put on

mine," he offered, taking off the big overcoat again.
"No, I'll be fine. Never feel the cold," she lied.
"You'll soon see when you get outside."

Outside an icy blast of wind almost sent Hanna
sprawling to the ground.
The snow was still falling, driven by a strong wind.
"Now see if you need my coat or not," Mike said,
removing the great coat again.
"But now you'll be frozen," she protested. "Just
'till we get to the bus then." As she snuggled into
the huge coat, she thought Mike was something
between splendid and handsome, and exciting.
When they reached the bus they saw two men
pushing it from behind.
"It's stuck in a snow-drift and there's not a kick in
the engine," the man in the rubber boots
announced.
Twenty minutes later they set out to walk home
through the snow.
"I'll keep trying to get her started and catch up with
you," the bus driver called after them.

When they had walked for what seemed hours,
they stopped at a wayside cottage. Exhaustion,
cold, and desperation drove them to knock at the
door of the darkened cottage. Not even a glimmer
of light shone from within as they waited. Another
knock - and a rumbling sound. Then a welcome

light shone out of a lower room window.

Then the door creaked open a few inches.

"Who's there?" a female voice asked.

"We were at the dance in Connolly's barn. An' the bus broke down. We're sorry to knock this late. But we're frozen."

With that the door opened wider and a torch light shone out.

"Come on in. I'll get the fire going."

When the fire was lit, she went towards the bedroom, "I'll make myself decent while the kettle boils."

In no time she served us with steaming cups of tea and buttered oat-cakes.

"Now you're going to need some dry clothes. I know the very thing. Our Mary's Yankee trunk. Come and give me a lift with it," she said to Mike. With the big black trunk in the middle of the floor, she began sifting through it. "Our Mary spent forty years in New York and when she came back to retire she brought all these clothes with her. No good to anyone here; nobody would wear them." The smell of mothballs was overwhelming as she began distributing the clothes amongst us.

Half an hour later, we set out again, warm and dry dressed in Aunt Mary's Yankee clothes. "We look like ghosts from another time," Hanna commented, as they waded with silenced footsteps through the deep snow.

When they reached the cross-roads, Mike kissed her goodbye. "I'm off to America on Wednesday," he told her, with a sudden sadness in his tone. "But I'll never forget you … an' I'll never forget tonight."

Now looking at the fur wrap through misted eyes Hanna could have sworn that the glass eyes winked at her.

Smuggling

Seated beside Jane on the bus on a bright July morning, going on her annual outing to Derry, I could barely contain my excitement. Since Jane asked me to go with her, I had anticipated every bump of the way with mounting glee. "I picked a good day for it. I think it's going to be a scorcher,"

Jane said, with a broad smile of pleasure. When
the bus pulled in by the roadside to pick up two
more passengers Jane hastily tucked her feet with
the old worn shoes on them under the seat. "I don't
want anybody to see these old shoes or they will
think I'm down and out. I can't wait to get the new
ones, and chuck these in the Foyle.
Them customs men are only a damned torture," she
grumbled, as the bus trundled off again.
When we finally arrived in Derry the sun was high
in the sky, and the temperature climbing with it.
By the time we reached the top of Shipquay Street,
great beads of sweat had broken out on Jane's
forehead. In the shoe-shop she took an age to
decide on which pair of shoes to buy. When she
finally made her choice, she said to the assistant,
"don't bother with the box, for I'll be wearing them
now. The damned customs you see."
Finally, with the old shoes in a brown paper bag,
we set off down towards the Foyle. "There goes
the relics of oul' decency," she said, as they hit the
water with a splash.
Then, picking up a piece of mud from the ground
with her hankie, she smeared it over the new shoes.
"There, that should fool them," she said, with a nod
of satisfaction.
As the day wore on Jane's purchases mounted. She
couldn't resist the wool coat in the sale, "I'll never
get a bargain like that again. And won't I be glad

of it on a winter's day."

Neither could she resist buying the heavy woollen jumper for Johnny; or the warm cardigan.

"Now we will go up to the City Café for something to eat, and we can put these clothes on and get rid of the paper bags," she announced at last. While in the café I felt sick and sweaty. Later in the ladies toilet I happened to glance at myself in the mirror, and saw the angry looking red spots on my face and neck. When I showed them to Jane, and she had scrutinised them thoroughly, she said, "Chicken pox. Aye I'm sure that's chicken pox." When we left the café, Jane was dressed in Johnnie's woollen jumper, and on top, her new woollen coat, with numerous items concealed on her person, while I wore the big woollen cardigan with items of underwear stuffed underneath. With the afternoon sun beating down we finally reached the bus-stop, exhausted and perspiring.

Tension was mounting as the bus neared the custom post. "Just act casual. We have nothing to declare," she whispered as the customs officer climbed into the bus. I could feel the sweat break out on my brow, and the chicken pox itch like they were on fire, while I watched his beady eyes scrutinise the passengers. When he reached our seat he came to a halt. "It's hardly a day for wearing a woollen coat Madam," he commented, as he looked us up and down. Looking up at him, Jane gave him an innocent smile, before she said, "Aye, it has turned out to be a right day after all. But when I left this morning, there was a wind that would skin a fairy." Then his eyes settled on me. As he looked me up and down, I couldn't help thinking what a picture I must have looked, with my red spots, sweaty face, and the big woollen cardigan puffed out at the chest with Jane's new knickers. His next words proved that I was right to fear the worst. "Would you both mind following me into the office?"

"Oh, I can't think what for. But all right," Jane said.

As I followed her down the aisle of the bus, I could feel my mouth dry up, my legs shake, and in that moment I wished with all my heart that I was back home.

Inside the customs office Jane babbled on about the change in the weather since we set off in the morning, giving the customs man few opportunities to get a word in. Then grabbing me by the shoulder, she pushed me gently towards him.

"Look at this poor wee girl. She's been hot and feverish all day, and now she's come out in these funny spots." Then leaning towards him she whispered, "I think it could be the small pox. Do you think you would be able to recognise the spots?" He instantly jerked backwards, a look of fear in his eyes. I could feel my face blaze with humiliation as his hostile eyes met mine. "Go on, get back on the bus. I'll be watching for you again," he said angrily.

When the bus was well out of sight Jane shed the coat and jumper, and I the big cardigan and the knickers from under my blouse with relief. "I don't think he believed that I had small pox. I felt worse than a leper."

"Ah well, God moves in mysterious ways. Because if you hadn't sprouted them spots, we could have lost all," she said with a mischievous grin.

Waltzing, Green Apples and Woodbine

We sat down under the big oak tree, to wait for

Pat the barber on his way to the village. In the distance
we could hear the trundle of horse-carts, making their
way home laden with barrels of water from the river.
July and early August had witnessed the driest spell
of weather in many years, drying up springs and

streams in its wake.

John nursed his money tin protectively on his knee, while he moved his legs up and down impatiently, causing the coins inside to rattle.

He opened the tin, and began counting the money in loud whispers. "Not again. I've watched you count that damned money three times today already."

"Oh, will you shut up. Now I'll have to start again," he grumbled.

"What are you going to buy with it anyway?"

"A gun and holster; sure I told you before. Now will you keep your mouth closed, 'till I count it."

At the head of the brae, a lone cyclist appeared out of the shady clump of trees. As Pat cycled up to us, John hastily put his coins back in the box before he had time to finish counting them.

When the barber's work was done, we all set off for the village, some on bicycles and others on foot.

When we reached the village, Kate and I were attracted to the sounds of music coming from the wee hall. Peering through the door we watched as twenty or so couples danced around the floor, and in between the bursts of music, came a hub of Scottish accents. When the music began again we slid quietly inside, and sat down on one of the long benches inside the door. The dancers were in high spirits, but much to our annoyance most of them were middle aged.

At the same time as the drummer announced an old time waltz, we noticed three youths sitting in the opposite corner, one was dark and mysterious looking. As the waltz began, two of them came over and asked us to dance. I ended up with the one who had ginger hair and a spotty face; while the dark mysterious looking one remained in the corner, much to my disappointment. As we began the dance and I felt my feet tripping over his again, and again, I vowed that I would learn to waltz properly. When the ordeal was over I could only feel a great sense of relief. As we sat down again someone announced over the microphone, "Hamish will now play us a few tunes on the bagpipes." The buzzing of the bagpipe's drones, like a swarm of angry bees swamped the interruption. When we had endured this for a decent interval, we made our escape quietly.

Walking home in the twilight I vowed again that I would learn to waltz. In my head, I had a mental picture of myself gliding around the floor gracefully in white satin with the dark mysterious looking Scottish fellow.

We walked side by side in silence lost in our secret thoughts, and sniffing the sweet smell of honeysuckle by the roadside as we went.

As we passed Mc Goughan's apple garden we heard voices coming from the other side of the wall. Stopping to listen, I recognised John's voice. Climbing over the wall I could see the red glow of lighted cigarettes.

"Wait until I get home and tell that you were

smoking," I said watching them jump in surprise.
Then he shouted back, "mind your own business, and stop spying on us."

About a hundred yards from home he caught up with us. "Please don't tell them about the smoking," he pleaded, the earlier bravado all gone.

"Who was that with you; and what were you doing in that garden? And where did you get the cigarettes?"

"Johnny Murphy and me bought twenty Woodbine between us. We went in to get a few apples out of Mick's garden," he hurriedly explained.

"How many of the cigarettes did you smoke?"

"Ten each. We just lit one off the other 'till they were all smoked. Promise you'll say nothing. If you promise, then I'll promise to tell nothing on you, ever again."

"All right, I'll keep my mouth shut."

"But you reek of tobacco, and they might smell it," Kate warned, as we reached the door.

They were in deep conversation with a visiting neighbour, when we went into the kitchen, and hardly noticed our entrance.

Later when there was a lull in the conversation I asked, "Do you know where I could learn how to waltz?"

Peering at me from over the top of his glasses, Robert said, "I used to be a dab hand at waltzing myself. Maybe I could teach you."

"Right then. When will we start?"

"No time like the present, I suppose," he said with a

grin. Before the lesson could begin we needed to find suitable music. After sifting through the record collection we finally came up with 'The Pride of Erin Waltz' on an old scratchy seventy-eight.

The lesson was barely underway when we heard a thud, and saw John fall to the floor, looking white as chalk, and deathly still where he lay.

Lifting him up my father carried him outside to the fresh air; my mother following behind in a state of panic while 'The Pride of Erin Waltz' got stuck in a groove, repeating the same few bars eerily. I could feel panic rising, wondering if Woodbine and green apples could prove fatal. Just as I had decided to break my promise not to tell, they came back through the door with John back on his feet again, still looking pale and a little shaky; but alive.

"How many cigarettes did you smoke? And how many green apples did you eat?" Robert asked him, as he guided him to the chair by the fire.

"How did you know?" I asked in astonishment.

"Wasn't hard to work out. He stinks of tobacco and as for the green apples.... well, I don't need to go into details."

The waltzing lessons continued for the rest of the week until I had mastered the art; but not before my mother had threatened to leave home. "If I hear that confounded scratchy racket one more time, I'm leaving," she threatened more than once, while we tripped around the kitchen floor.

Hazel McIntyre

At last brimming with confidence, and dressed in my best frock, Kate and I set off for the wee hall. The same holiday-makers we saw the first night were there again, and in the corner sat the same three young lads. Each time the dark and mysterious looking one glanced in my direction, I gave him a shy smile of encouragement, and hoped that he would ask me to waltz with him.

After we had suffered Hamish on the bagpipes, and dutifully clapped, the drummer announced an old time waltz. The smiles must have worked, because the dark and mysterious looking lad came over and asked me to dance. My heart skipped a beat as we took the floor, eager to show off my new-found skill.

It took only a matter of seconds to know that he had two left feet. As we stumbled across the floor, first one foot and then the other came down heavily on mine causing an agony of sudden pain, and I felt the sweat break out on my brow with each new agony, while I prayed for the dance to end.

When the waltz was finally over I babbled my thanks, and in that moment of pain he had lost all his former mystery and romance.

Dark Recollections

James walked on ahead with shoulders hunched,

the May morning sun lighting the auburn tinges in
his hair. An air of gloom seemed to descend on all,
as they approached the gates of the grey
schoolhouse.
The memory of yesterday sent prickles of fright down
James's spine, as he stood momentarily by the gate
feeling the warm sun on his face. The memory made

him want to run as far away from the school as possible.

The schoolmaster paced up and down beside the desks banging his fist periodically on the wooden desks, making the ink-wells jump, and shouting his familiar threats.

"You are a lazy, useless bunch. And I'll get some knowledge into your thick heads before this inspector comes. One way or another, I'll get information into your thick skulls."

With relief they heard him leave the classroom, banging the door as he went. But the relief was short lived, when a few minutes later he returned carrying a small branch from a sycamore tree, with its lime green spring leaves still attached.

From his pocket he took a penknife, and began peeling off the leaves, slowly and methodically. When he had finished he viewed his work in silence. Then holding it in his right hand, he tapped his left hand rhythmically, with a nod of satisfaction.

Getting to his feet, he cleared his throat, and spoke again in a quieter tone that conveyed more menace than his earlier shouts had. "When the inspector comes, I want each of you to tell him this story in Irish. Word perfect, mind you. I'm going to write it down on the blackboard. You will then copy it, and learn it by tomorrow." Then he carefully lifted the newly peeled stick from the desk, and in a voice chilled with menace, he said, "The pupil who dares not to have learned this story by tomorrow morning will feel the full, agonising...might of this stick on both hands.... six times each."

Then in an almost sweet voice, he said, "we will get to work."

Now, weak with fear, the class stood in a row, every muscle tense and minds that tried desperately to remember what they had struggled to learn the night before.

With stick in hand the teacher walked up and down the row, in silence. "Your turn first Johnny." he said. Clearing his throat, and with a tremor in his voice, Johnny stumbled through the first two paragraphs. And then silent. "Stuck already? I'll give you one more chance." Repeating the first word of the next sentence twice, with no response from Johnny, he ordered, "hold out your hand!" Standing beside him James felt paralysed by fear, as the sickening thuds of the cane came down mercilessly on Johnny's hands. "Your turn James." James opened his mouth, but no sound came. Licking his lips he tried again; again nothing. Somehow he managed to blot out the pain that followed, and all the time his mind cried out for revenge. He stayed up until the wee hours the night before, and learned the story off by heart, and this knowledge made the injustice all the more unbearable.

The inspector came three days later. When the

formal greetings were over, James sat glued to his seat, waiting once more with fear for the dreaded Irish story to raise it's frightening head. Instead the inspector's words and his easy manner surprised him. Standing in front of the class, and with a friendly smile he began, "Now class I want to test your powers of imagination. So I am asking you to write me a short essay. Any subject you like. A ghost story perhaps?" he added, with a quizzical frown.

Five minutes later James sat motionless, having just written two short sentences. As the inspector stood over him he could feel the beads of sweat break out on his feverish brow.

"Run out of steam already?" he inquired. James shook his head slowly, then licking his dry lips he answered in an almost whisper, "I'm not sure how to spell amazement." Walking back to the front of the class he cleared his throat, and then tapped the desk loudly with a ruler. "Your attention for a moment please. The pupil in the second desk stopped writing because he was afraid of making a spelling mistake. None of us would ever learn anything if we were afraid to make a mistake. We learn by our mistakes. And, if we are wise we avoid making the same mistake twice. Back to the essay then."

Freed from the fear of making a mistake, James began his essay. When he had finished the inspector chose his efforts as being the most imaginative and read it aloud to the class.

Echoes of Another Time

Thirty years on, James felt a compulsion to return to the, by now, long derelict schoolhouse. The rotting door creaked eerily on its rusty hinges as he walked through. The sound of his feet echoed in the emptiness. He had the feeling of standing in utter loneliness. He could hear the sounds of the cane, as though from an immense distance. James could hear the blood singing in his ears; he was a helpless child again, opening his mouth when no sound came out. With a suddenness that surprised even him, he screamed loudly at the emptiness.

Outside again, he stood by the rusting gate resting his hand on the stone wall. As he watched it all seemed to shrink before his gaze. The wall, the gate, the grey schoolhouse itself suddenly seemed not to be the big, frightening place he remembered. Then he said aloud to the emptiness, "I made a success of my life. Not because of you, but in spite of you."

Late Home

Rounding the bend in the lane, we saw Ellen's bent figure leant over on the garden gate. Getting down from our bicycles, we stopped for a chat.

"Why did he leave it so long?" she asked, her eyes fixed on the black car, that slowly made its way up the steep brae and out of sight.

"What is the use of coming back now, when all belonging to him is dead and gone? He has me grieving all over again for friends that I thought I had finished grieving for," she said with a sad note in her voice while she continued to stare at the empty brae. "Who?" I asked. "Who are you talking about?"

"Harry Mc Sweeney," she said, her eyes still scanning the empty lane, long after the car had disappeared.

As we had never heard of Harry Mc Sweeney, or anyone belonging to him, we went on our way.

We had forgotten all about Harry until we encountered him on a warm afternoon in May, when he offered us a lift home from the town. "I'm Harry Mc Sweeney," he said as we got seated in the black Ford. He was a lean, bronzed man, with a face that might have been carved out of bog oak. When he discovered who we were, and where we were going, he said, "I'm going out to see Ellen, so I can take you that far. I must make a stop on the way; won't take long. I'm restoring the old homestead," he went on. "But it's so hard to get things done around here. I've been away too long, I guess," he added with a shake of his head.

"I was scarcely seventeen when I left home. I wanted to see a bit of the world, make my fortune, and come home again. That was fifty years ago, and I've only now made it back. Trouble is nearly everybody I knew has died, or gone away." At the top of the hill he stopped the car suddenly. "I have seen this sight in my dreams over and over again. Dreamt I was back many a time, only to wake up in the Australian outback, or the Arizona desert," he said wistfully.

His eyes were fixed ahead on the landscape of small fields, cut up by hedges and stone ditches that zigzagged over the slopes, laying in patches of vivid greens, and yellow whin blossom. And the grey streak of road dividing the landscape, stretching in long loops, far away like a river crawling down from the hills on its way to the sea.

Turning around in the seat he looked at us for a moment and said, "Trouble is we take everything for granted, until it's not there anymore." Then he started the engine and drove on down the hill.

Then driving up a lane-way he stopped the car, and got out. Mick Murphy appeared around the corner of the house.

"Oh, it's yourself Harry. Grand day," he greeted him. "I've come about the plumbing that you promised to do for me," he continued.

Then he went on to list his complaints; taps that constantly dripped, air locks, and leaks. "Like I said before, it wants new washers, a thorough overhaul in fact."

"When can you get it done? I've been waiting for weeks as it is," Harry said indignantly.

Mick smiled like an angel. "Well, I haven't managed to get the parts yet," he said.

"When will you get them? Well?" persisted Harry impatiently. Mick stroked the side of his chin thoughtfully, and smiled back charmingly, before saying, "about three weeks or so."

"Three weeks! I told you my daughter's coming for a holiday in ten days," Harry said angrily.

Rubbing his jaw again, Mick said gently, "I'm doing my best, aye, I'm doing my best for you."

Looking baffled and furious, Harry got back into the car and drove off. He grumbled and complained about local incompetence for the remainder of the journey.

When we arrived at Ellen's cottage we were glad to get out of the car, and away from the sound of his complaining voice. "Come in for a wee cup of tea, girls," Ellen offered when she saw us. Once inside Harry began his complaints about Mick, and local incompetence all over again.

"Like I told you before Harry, things move at a slower pace here. You will just have to be patient like the rest of us." Ellen scolded.

When we had finished our tea, and were about to leave, Harry said "I'm having a party when my daughter arrives. And you're invited." At this bit of news we warmed to him a little, after all a party was a party, and we were always on the lookout for somewhere to go.

The invitation to the party arrived in the post two weeks later. As it was the first formal invitation we ever had, we felt quite pleased, and important.

Dressed in our starched cotton frocks, we set off to cycle the five miles to Harry's house-party.

We had ridden about two miles when the rain came,

lightly at first, but it soon turned into a deluge. And so we arrived at Harry's party bedraggled, and soaked to the skin, only to find the house in darkness. "Oh, good Lord, we have only come on the wrong night!" Hanna wailed.

Going over to the window, I peered into the dim interior and saw the red glow from the fire. Then going over to the door I knocked loudly, and waited. "Come in. It's open," Harry's voice shouted back. He was sitting in a chair gazing gloomily into the fire. When he finally looked up and saw us he said, "God bless my soul. I forgot all about you two. The party is cancelled. I went round to tell the others, but I forgot about you." He peered at us for a minute, and we could see the beginnings of amusement in his eyes. Then he began a smile that turned to bellows of laughter. I could feel the hot flushes of anger rising up inside me, as I shouted, "It's not funny. We're soaked through and frozen;" "Oh, I'm sorry. It's just that you look such sorry sights," he broke off again into roars of laughter, which only deepened our resentment of him. Then getting up from the chair he switched on the light before he said, "go on, take a look in the mirror." Glowering at my reflection, I saw a face barely recognisable as my own. The mascara I had carefully applied ran down my face in black streaks, and wet strands of hair clung around my face like spider's webs.

Looking back at Hanna's bedraggled appearance,

similar to my own, we forgot our discomfort and disappointment and giggled simultaneously.

"The party was cancelled because my daughter won't be able to make it for another week. I'm really sorry for dragging you all this way on a night like this for nothing," he said handing us a towel each. Then dragging two chairs close to the fire he said, "come and get warmed up, then I'll drive you home."

We sat in silence for a while, our eyes fixed on the blazing fire. Glancing across at Harry I saw his face creased into a set of earnest wrinkles. Hanna cleared her throat self-consciously before she asked, "have you settled in yet?" "As settled as I'm going to be, I suppose. I stayed away too long. Ellen was right on that score. Trouble is, I wanted things to be the same as they were before I left. And that's not realistic... is it?" he asked.

Then going over to a shelf he came back with a brown folder, and sat down again. "This is a photo of my grandsons. About your ages I'd say. They are coming here next week with their mother. And I'll be relying on you two, to entertain them. Take them to a dance or two with you... that sort of thing." As we gazed at the two handsome faces looking back at us from the photograph, our mood changed for the better.

"We'll be glad to help," Hanna said, looking up at him. Harry's homecoming was turning into a blessing in disguise. "Good looking lads eh? They have their grandmother's green eyes. First thing I noticed about Sally when we first met in New York, was her amazing green eyes."

"Was Sally your wife?"

"Aye, she was my wife. Died three years ago. I still miss her so much. She was the most beautiful, intelligent and witty woman that ever lived. And she spent her life with a miserable oul' coot like me." His eyes misted up as he spoke.

Of late he had come to realise that he had lived most of his life enveloped in the dream world of an imaginative child, long after childhood was past. Now that its mists were swept away by the death of Sally, he was having to face the chill necessity of living alone for the first time in over fifty years. Reaching back into the folder, he took out a large photograph and carefully took off the tissue paper surrounding it. He gazed at it intently for a while before handing it across to Hanna, "Sally and me on our wedding day."

The photograph showed a handsome young couple in a formal pose. "She was beautiful. And you weren't so bad yourself," Hanna said. As the flickering fire-light lit up his craggy, weather-beaten face, we felt a new sympathy and understanding for this crabbit old man.

"Better give you that lift home. Hope that bloody oul' car will start. Nothing in this place seems to work the way it should. I'll soon need new tyres; dam' roads are so full of holes." In the back seat,

Echoes of Another Time

Hanna had a sudden image of the two good looking grandsons, with youthful voices, that grumbled on and on and on.

The Visit

After climbing the big hill they could see the massive pillars of the entrance. "This is it," Grace said, "I was only wee when I was here last. But, this is it." As they opened the creaky, rusted gates that heralded the entrance to the dark, dank avenue Hanna's heart sank. The thought of spending a day and night in this dark, depressing place was making her regret her decision to come. The rain had turned the driveway dark and muted the colours of the surrounding hills.

"Please come with me. Please. I've never been on two bus rides by myself, and my mother says I must go because Auntie Grace's husband had a stroke. And my mother can't go because of wee Joe," her voice trailed off. "Please," Grace had pleaded, a few days earlier. And now, here they were walking amongst the dark, dripping trees, in the middle of nowhere.

Suddenly, the house appeared, huge and almost majestic from a distance.

Close up, the overgrown driveway and peeling paint told its own story.

They stood silently gazing at the crumbling façade for a minute or so, then Hanna asked, "How did your aunt end up in a big place like this?"

"My mother said she came here to work just after 'The Emergency' and ended up marrying the son. She had nothing but hard work and resentment from his mother, Mammy often told us."

"Suppose we better go in," Grace said, with a sigh.

They climbed the moss-covered, stone steps to the big oak door, and pulled a bell-rope. The rotting rope unravelled and the iron pull fell to the ground with a clang. "Looks like nobody uses this door anymore," Grace commented.

Just then, the great door creaked open and a slim

woman with greying, auburn hair and deep-set blue
eyes, stood between the huge door-posts.

"Thought I heard something out here. Come in.
Come in. You're both most welcome. And wee
Grace has grown up. I'd hardly recognise you."
Inside the hall they looked around. It smelt of
beeswax and lavender and unlike the outside
showed little sign of neglect. Old portraits hung
from the walls and in the far corner a grandfather
clock chimed three.

Hanna thought the whole scene echoed of other
times and she wanted to know about its past.

As though reading her thoughts, Margaret said, "I'll
tell you all about the place later when you've had
some tea and talked to Jeffrey. He's been waiting to
see you."

They drank tea and ate home-made scones in a big,
old-fashioned kitchen, with a gleaming black range
flanked on each side by easy-chairs.

"We spend most of our time in here. The range
provides heat as well as the cooking. We had very
few turf last winter and coal's so costly," she
explained. "Now if you've finished your tea we'll
go and see Jeffrey.

You know he's had a stroke?" They nodded.

"Well, his speech is still a bit slurred and he has
very little use of his left hand. But, he'll be
delighted to see you."

They followed her to the far end of the hall.

Opening a door she said, "Jeffery, look who's here to see you!"

He was seated at a blazing turf fire, his greying hair curling over the collar of his white shirt. He got to his feet with the aid of a walking stick, and the eyes that met theirs were gentle.

"Welcome. You … you're welcome," he greeted them, his voice a little slurred.

"The girls can stay and talk to you while I get your tea," Margaret said, smiling at him.

"Don't know what I'd do … without Margaret," he said, when she'd gone.

Grace did most of the talking to start with. They talked about the bus journey and about the weather until Hanna asked, "Have you lived here all your life?" He nodded. "Most of it. Apart from when I done a bit of travelling. Then there was the war. Awful business, war." He gazed into the fire in silence for a while, a pained look on his face. "Aye, the old house like myself has seen better days. I hate not being able to do my share. Poor Margaret does everything. She deserved better than she got. A whole lot better than she got," he repeated.

"It's a nice big house. Who are all the people in the portraits?" Grace asked.

"Ancestors. Don't … hardly want to remember one of them. I wanted Margaret to take them down. She said they belong here. If I'd been shunned the way she was, I'd want to burn every last one." He shook his head and stared into the distance. Hanna wanted to hear more about the past and his ancestors. But he changed the subject.

They noticed that apart from the occasional slurred word, his speech had become almost normal.

 When Margaret brought his tea, they went back to the kitchen.

"I must say you've perked him up. Nothing like youth to lift the spirits."

They watched her prepare vegetables at the table. Hanna offered to help.

"No, no. You sit and rest yourselves. We have our dinner here in the evening. Old tradition, that I carried on. I usually take Jeffrey out for a walk in the wheelchair in the afternoon. It's too wet today though."

"If it dries up we'll take him," Grace offered.

"Thanks, that would be a great help. Looking after Jeff an' this old house takes me all my time."

"How long have you lived here?" Hanna asked, hoping she would tell her more about her past.

"I first came here when I was twenty-two. I trained as a nurse in London and came back to Ireland during the war. I was employed here to nurse Jeffrey's grandmother. By the time she died … Jeff and I had fallen in love. It went down bad with his mother. Very bad."

"Why?" Hanna ventured.

"Oh, I was from the wrong background I suppose.

Anyhow, she made life hard for us for a while.
Then when she got cancer, I was the one she
wanted to look after her. Strange that." She paused
for a moment chewing on her upper lip. "Near the
end she asked me to forgive her for all the harsh
words. I forgave her. She was just a product of her
time.
Jeffrey remains bitter though. Feels I was very
badly treated.
Anyway, that's all past. Come, and I'll show you
where you're sleeping."

They followed her upstairs and along a wood-
panelled corridor. The room was huge with bay
windows overlooking the village on one side and a
pond on the other. "Jeffrey's old room," Margaret
explained, "hope you'll be comfortable."
"I've never seen such a big bedroom," Grace said,
when she shut the door. They admired the big,
ornate furniture, the old velvet drapes and old
photographs and leather-bound books that echoed
of other days.
"I wish she had told me more about the past,"
Hanna said, as she looked at an old photograph of
Jeffrey in an Air-Force uniform. "He was good
looking," Grace commented. Hanna absently
reached up for one of the leather-bound books from
a shelf. As she opened it, a photograph that had
been encased between its pages fell to the ground,

"Look at this one," Hanna said, excitedly. "He's with another girl … a blonde."

While they were still looking at the photograph, Margaret came back into the room carrying two Eiderdowns. "What photograph is that?" she asked, coming over to where they sat on the bed.

"I was looking for a book … to read and it fell out," Hanna stammered.

Taking the photograph from Hanna, Margaret stared at it for what seemed an age, while Hanna and Grace exchanged uneasy glances.

Finally Margaret gave a deep sigh, "Jeffrey had destroyed all the photographs of her long ago. This one must have escaped." Then meeting their glances she said, "She was his fiancée once. Her name was Jean. Anyhow, you may not have noticed that Jeffrey has only one leg. He lost a leg during the war. Well, Jean couldn't cope with it … repulsed by it. The first time she saw what remained … she ran from the room." She sighed deeply again.

"His mother approved of Jean too. It had a bad effect on him. Lost all his confidence for a long time after that."

Then she looked at each of them sternly. "For God's sake don't go telling him that I told you any of this."

"No. We wouldn't say a word … honest."

She glanced at the photograph again with a look of

sadness.

When the rain stopped, they took Jeffrey out for a walk in the wheelchair.

As they passed a church near the village, Jeffrey commented, "That's where we got married. She was the most beautiful bride, and it was without a doubt the happiest day of my life. Margaret restored my faith in humanity."

As they neared the back door, he suddenly put the brakes on the wheelchair. "I'm going to walk into the house. I've been practising in my room. Margaret doesn't know."

He slowly rose from the chair and walked, a little unsteadily at first, towards the back door.

Turning around from the stove, she gazed at him dizzily for a moment, then a smile that transformed her features spread across her face and her eyes lit up.

"Jeff you've done it! You're a warrior and no mistake."

While Hanna and Grace looked on, she crossed the space between them and threw her arms around his waist.

Margaret walked with them to the big gates the following morning.

"We both want you to come back soon. You done us both a power of good," she said, when they reached the gates.

They kissed her goodbye and walked a few paces down the lane. Suddenly Hanna ran back to where she stood, "When we were out yesterday for the walk we passed a church. Well, Jeffrey said that you got married there. He said you were a beautiful bride … an' it was the happiest day of his life." Then pausing for breath, she went on, "It was nearly worth it to lose a leg … to get rid of that Jean one," she concluded.

Margaret looked at her for a few seconds, before bellowing with laughter.

Katie's Tales

"Who was she entertaining this evening...

Lawrence of Arabia?" my brother asked when he heard that we had been to see Katie.

Katie lived in a remote end of the Parish, with her husband Pat and her elder sister Margaret, who was deaf.

Katie's house was like a magnet to us in the early teenage years. She told wonderful, romantic stories about beautiful, glamorous people, where she was always the central figure. The events were glittering affairs set in romantic places like the south of France, Paris or Rome.

In her youth Katie had worked for a wealthy family, and travelled with them around the world. The most striking thing about her were her dark glowing eyes, that expressed every twist and turn that her stories took. Hanging on the wall of the parlour there hung a portrait of Katie in her youth. "I was just twenty when that was painted. He was a famous artist who painted portraits of the rich and famous," she often told us.

To her neighbours, Katie was a bit of an enigma, with a head full of romantic nonsense that bore no resemblance to the real world. They would say things like, "it's good for her, that she has nothing better to bother her." Katie must have been aware of this, because when a neighbour came in unexpectedly in the middle of one of her tales she would promptly change the subject and say. "Isn't it awful how the eggs have gone down in price?" or some such mundane comment, leaving us high and dry, not knowing what way the story would end. With the atmosphere completely changed, we would usually decide to leave, and hope that she would take up where she left off at a later date.

Echoes of Another Time

Katie's life changed completely when Pat had a sudden stroke, which left him partially paralysed. Katie took on the task of nursing her husband and running the farm herself, for which she won the admiration of the entire community. These changes in her life put an abrupt end to her story-telling, much to our sadness. We missed those happy entertaining flights of fancy in Katie's cosy kitchen; the cups of tea drank from delicate china cups, and the dainty wee buns that were part of the sense of occasion that Katie created for us.

Many years later while on a holiday we gathered again in Katie's house.
"I have never forgotten the happy hours we spent here," Hanna said. "You were a great story-teller."
Looking at us with a grin she said, "Aye, I suppose I was. Most of it was from my imagination. But some of it was true. Few of us get the life that in our youth we hoped for, and expected, but most of us, I dare say get the life best suited to us." Then she said quietly, "always hold on to your dreams and fantasies, for they see you through the dark days."

Before we left, she showed us the contents of her black trunk. To our amazement it was full of beautifully made silk evening dresses. "Now, I want each of you to choose one for yourself. There is bound to be a special occasion in the future when you will need one. And these dresses will never really date, they will always be in fashion," she assured us. We thanked her kindly, and as we made our choices, we could recognise each gown in turn from Katie's stories, and wondered again how much of what Katie told us was factual, and how much was fiction.

When the time came to leave with our treasures, she accompanied us outside, and as she passed the hen-house she said, "I must go in and see how my rooster is doing on the sitting of eggs."

"A rooster sitting on eggs!"

Looking into the hen-house, sure enough, there sat the rooster.

"Oh, aye. He broke his leg, and I couldn't have him sitting around all day doing nothing," she explained.

Katie's talents went away beyond imaginings.

Fear was the Weapon

T he missionaries came with touring caravans
towed by big black Ford motor cars, straining and
puffing black fumes from their exhausts; a rare
sight indeed in 1950's rural Inishowen. They set up
camp in a bare green field a mile or so from the
village. They were charismatic characters, who
went from house to house with their 'good news'
message, aimed at the young they said. The venue

was the village hall, they promised refreshments afterwards, and a choir. And so we set off through the quiet lanes on an early autumn evening to hear the 'good news' and avail of the refreshments.

The hall was almost full of children and teenagers when we arrived. A table at the rear was set with jugs of orange juice, small dainty sandwiches and biscuits. The choir began to sing sweetly, accompanied by a portable organ.

Then the preacher began to address us. To begin with his tone was low, his voice seductive, with an accent that crossed between the American deep south and south of the Bann. The subject was sin, punishment and the works of the devil. The devil awaited us at every turning point in our lives; he was luring us with rock 'n' roll, he was lurking in the TV screens that unwary people were installing in their homes. The work of the devil was everywhere; dancing was yet another pursuit where the devil frequented. Sin was everywhere. Then his voice rose to a higher pitch that vibrated the very building, "you know the pain of burning your small finger. Can you imagine your whole body burning forever throughout all eternity?" A mass shudder seemed to shake the wooden benches as the sheer terror of his words vibrated amongst the assembled youth, like the audience in a cinema watching unspeakable horrors on a screen. If the love and compassion of God was mentioned, none of us remembered it. And, when it was over we had lost our appetite for the refreshments.

We silently filed out into the darkness and walked home with our fearful thoughts on a vengeful God waiting to trip us up at every turn of the road. Was hell and damnation the price we would have to pay for watching 'Rawhide' through a snow-flurry on TV, or the sound of Buddy Holly, hissing his way through 'rave on' on the old wireless? And with the showband era getting into full swing, promising an image of jiving in winkle-picker shoes with sugar-starched petticoats swinging, my ten year old brain felt a gloom such as I had never known before. And so it seemed that avoiding the horrors of hell would mean forgoing every little pleasure that this life had to offer.

Time and reason allayed most of the terrors and showed God in a truer light, which enabled most of us to enjoy our childhood and youth. But, sometimes departed childhood awakes and we reach into that special cupboard of the mind, where we thought we safely stored our fears, only to find their dark echoes still there.

All religions were guilty, to a greater or lesser extent, of using the tactics of fear and guilt as weapons of control. This left many of us with deeply buried fears and guilt. By taking these skeletons out of the cupboard we can recognise them for what they are, and so lay them to rest.

A City Man's Gifts

The neat rows of standard roses we had so carefully planted the evening before were now mere twigs, denuded of every last bud and leaf, their plastic labels flapping mockingly in the early morning light. Then I spied him. 'Ginty,' my other half from the big city's recently acquired goat. "What did I tell you about that damned goat?" I stormed. "We won't have a plant left. You-must-get-rid-of-it!"

"The fence would need to be higher," the other half, said sheepishly.

"I-want-rid-of-it!" I screamed back.

Half an hour later my eight-year-old son knocked gingerly on the kitchen door. Sitting there, on his hunkers, with one arm around 'Ginty' he said sweetly, "Ginty says he's sorry. He didn't know they were flowers. Says, he won't do it again." As I looked at that pleading expression in his eyes, I knew that 'Ginty' was here to stay and that I was in the minority of one. Noah's ark had come to rest on our remote Donegal hillside.

It all began with chickens. "It would be nice to have a few chickens. They would give us nice fresh eggs," my London bred spouse announced, shortly after arriving in Donegal.

"I want no dirty chickens," I protested. I'd seen enough hens in my youth, growing up as I did on a farm near Culdaff. I'd cleaned more dirty eggs and scraped up more hen-droppings than I cared to remember.

But he was very persuasive, and in the end it was agreed that if he constructed a hen-coop with a high fence, he could have the hens.

A week or so later, he purchased a dozen hens, a rooster and six ducks from a county Antrim farmer he had met in the course of his business. They were put in sacks with holes punched in them, for easy breathing. And so, on a grey early winter's night, he set off for home delighted with his new feathered friends. He had just crossed the border at Muff, when a car pulled out from a laneway and flashed him down. Two customs officers in uniform came up to the driver's window, "anything to declare sir?"

"Nothing at all."

"Will you get out and open your boot?"

When he had opened the boot, the officer peered in, and on seeing the sacks asked, "What have you here sir?"

"Hens in one. Ducks in the other," replied the spouse. The customs man glanced at his colleague, and with a knowing nod said, "he says, he's got ducks in one sack - and hens in the other."

Then his tone became more aggressive, "open them!" he ordered. As the patient spouse untied the top of the first sack he warned, "Be careful in case they get out."

"Just get on with it!" the officer said, impatiently. When the sacks were opened, the customs man gingerly put his hand inside. Disturbed at the unwanted intrusion, and anxious to protect his harem, the irate rooster flapped his wings and lashed out with his sharp beak. He jumped backwards. "Bloody hell, it is hens," he shouted, retrieving his hand at speed, and rubbing it against his trouser leg.

"You're not supposed to take live poultry across the border," he added, furiously. The spouse's brow broke out in a sweat of panic, at the mere thought of having his precious feathered friends taken from him.

"I just bought them for a few fresh eggs. They're very healthy," he added, with a note of apology. Apart from the odd cackle and quack, there was a moment of silence.

"Go on. If I come across you smuggling poultry again I'll seize them, an' fine you into the bargain," he warned, as he got back into the car.

At the first glint of dawn, the rooster greeted us loudly the following morning and every subsequent morning until he died from old age.

A few weeks later he bought a ewe for the princely sum of eight pounds. On hearing about the newest arrival, a neighbouring farmer came to see it. With a puzzled frown, he took a long look at the sheep, and then looked into her mouth. Straightening up he rubbed his chin thoughtfully before he asked, "what oul' nave sold you that thing?"

"Why?" 'Himself' asked, surprised by the manner of the question.

"She's as oul' as the hills. She'll not survive the winter, because there's hardly a tooth in her head." While we were digesting this bad news, his next words cast an even deeper gloom.

"And she's blind in the right eye. Never make it through the winter if she can't graze. Aye, the nave that sold you that thing should be shot," he repeated, with a silent shake of the head.

Because of the absence of teeth, she was named 'Miss Gums' and she proved the farmer wrong by not only surviving the winter, but by also producing an offspring the following spring. The wise old sheep came to the kitchen door twice daily to be fed with softened food that compensated for her lack of teeth.

And so it was that 'Miss Gums' multiplied into a flock of sheep.

During the following year or so, 'Old Mc Donald,' wasn't in it. The spouse would arrive home from work, grinning from ear to ear. "You'll never guess what I got you?" he would say. I would look gingerly into the boot, and looking back at me, there would be the bright eyes of a kid goat, a pet lamb, a special breed of rabbit or some other creature in need of loving care. The children would jump for joy, while my heart would sink. Our endless procession of four legged friends grew bigger in size. When he rented a field to graze his first horse, they too multiplied when the new foals arrived.

Hazel McIntyre

As reflected in his gifts, my city man is a
countryman at heart.

Christmas Shoppers

Anna stood impatiently in the queue behind her loaded trolley and counted eight packed trolleys in front of her. Stamping her aching feet, she watched in the distance as assistants speedily and unceremoniously filled the plastic bags with goods, a hard look of impatience on their faces. Over the intercom 'Silent Night' bellowed out mournfully above the noise of wailing infants.

'Not much sign of the Christmas spirit here,' Anna sighed, leaning more heavily on her trolley for support. In that moment, she had an overwhelming desire to abandon her laden trolley and make a dash for the exit. Fighting mounting impatience she forced herself to remain calm. "It's a help in dark days to remember bright beginnings," a voice from long ago came back to her. From the queue next to her, she watched a man in an old tweed jacket move up beside her as she pushed her trolley into line. From his person came a sudden scent of pipe tobacco and cloves, and she breathed deeply and noisily of it, transforming her surroundings into a magical part of memory.

Gradually she became totally absorbed by the memory of a Christmas long ago, a memory that took her away from the modern, impersonal, hygienic supermarket, back through the mist of time to the rural Donegal village of her childhood. Back then the sunlight was brighter, brighter than it ever was before or will ever be again. The dance was swifter, moonlight more magical, colour more intense, and Christmas shook the soul to ecstasy.

Aunt Bea wrapped the woollen scarf around her neck before they set off on the two-mile walk to Mac's shop in the village. Anna had watched the old woman writing her Christmas shopping list for days, and now they were on their way. "We'll get

the hackney car back," she reassured Anna as they climbed the steep brae, the cold wind buffeting their faces. "I've had a hard life, if ever any woman had," she began as though talking to herself, "and yet," she went on, "with no reason for it, with every reason against it, my old heart still jumps for joy at Christmas time. And I am happy."
As darkness began to fall, they could see the light at Inistrahull lighthouse come and go, and Anna was convinced in her mind that it was caused by a giant waving a lantern.

Mac's shop was the biggest, and busiest in the village and sold everything from groceries to footwear, clothing, to knicker-elastic.
They entered the shop to the sharp clang of the bell and were greeted by John, the shop owner. Anna loved the mingling scents of smoked bacon, cloves, tobacco and snuff that greeted them.
She loved the hub of friendly voices, the sounds of the bacon slicer, and the click against the steel basin of the weighing scales. When a customer's sweets were weighed, Anna was handed three acid drops out of the jar. From deep within the house came the sound of carol singing, "choir practice" the shop owner explained, over the sound of the bacon slicer.
When the grocery part of the shopping was weighed neatly into the brown paper bags, the

whispering part of Aunt Bea's shopping began and Anna was encouraged to inspect the window display from outside the shop.

The sudden reflection of another presence made her jump. On closer inspection she recognised Maggie Molly, the long neck of a dead goose dangled from the opening in the straw bag she was carrying.

"It's a fine well fattened bird," she commented. "It's for young Mary Donnelly. She wanted it plucked, cleaned, singed and ready for the oven. Don't know what today's young women are coming to," she sniffed. Then picking up the goose again she walked away a few paces. "Oh, I nearly forgot. Tell your mother, Turkey Monday is on a Tuesday this year." As she walked away into the shadows, the dangling neck of the goose swayed eerily into time with her footsteps.

The sudden thud of a frozen turkey falling from the trolley in front of her jolted her thoughts rudely back to the present. The earlier impatience had left her and was replaced by a feeling of unexpected seasonal joy.

Wedding Fever

Spring came early that year. It came with the first soft southerly breeze, the first primroses, the first green hawthorn buds, crisp and sweet to eat and the first sounds of the Cuckoo.

Aunt Bea sat by the window waiting for the postman to make an appearance.

"Fancy him being late again on a grand day like this." Each day she spent up to two hours gazing at the distant road in wait for the post. About fifteen minutes later she spotted him cycling down the brae. She waited until he appeared over the wee hill near the house before she spoke, "he's got something for us anyhow," she said, rising from her window position and resuming her seat by the range to wait.

"This is some day," Jimmy said, opening his big canvas bag. When he had handed over the letters, he sat down to wait for his customary cup of tea. At last the letters were opened and silence prevailed during the reading.

"Some of us have been invited to Kate's wedding," Marie announced. I heard that two-hundred people have been invited.

"I hope I wasn't asked. For I'm passed weddings and big crowds."

"Has John and me been invited?" Hanna asked, not daring to hope.

"Just the three oldest, your father and me." Hanna ran outside, as tears of disappointment sprang into her eyes.

On the day of the wedding dark clouds scurried across the sky and the rain beat down against the window-panes. Hanna and John were in low spirits. "Bad enough not getting to the wedding. But now we can't even get outside," Hanna moaned, gazing bleakly out the window.

"Don't be so miserable you two. We'll find

something to pass the time. How about having a look through my old black trunk? We might find something that will interest you."

In the upper room she trailed the old trunk under the window and unlocked it.

"Poor girl, fancy her getting a day like this for her wedding," she commented, glancing again at the rain. "Two-hundred people and a fancy hotel. I bet it will cost the price of a wee farm too." Then a broad smile crossed her old face. "I know. I'll tell you a true wedding story that'll give you a laugh."

The two women turned the corner and slowly made their way up the narrow lane in silence. The two-mile walk up-hill from church tired them - slowing their steps.

From her cottage window Sally watched their backs gradually disappearing. "That feather looks ridiculous," she muttered to herself.

"She must have worn that same coat and hat on Sundays and fair days for the best part of twenty years at least." Sally looked skywards as if seeking divine inspiration. The blue feather poked up above the hat at a jaunty angle and wiggled as Maggie walked.

Maggie and her spinster daughter Mary were causing quite a stir amongst their neighbours at this time. The news of Mary's wedding, coming unexpected as it did, caused the commotion.

Hazel McIntyre

Weddings were common enough occurrences, but this one was different.

Mary, coming up on forty and with no great claim to beauty was considered to be well and truly on the shelf when Johnny McGlinn came on the scene and proposed to her. True, he was fifty if he was a day, and his joints creaked when he walked, but he had a farm and a bit of money; or so they said.

Then there was Maggie, Mary's mother. She was known far and wide for her meanness. Parting her from her money was like prizing a barnacle from a rock. She was a tall thin woman, with a long nose and sharp brown eyes. Her neighbours admired many of her qualities. At times of sickness, death, births or any other trouble, she was often called upon for assistance. Her calm efficiency and good sense were greatly appreciated at times of crisis in her townland. However, her advice on economic matters was scorned. "Every penny is a prisoner with her," was the usual remark from her neighbours. According to Maggie, new clothes were an unnecessary extravagance – 'make do and mend' was her motto.

Wedding clothes were on Mary's mind at that moment. She knew that she must talk to her mother about it that very day. She watched her mother as she carefully piled the turf around the naked coals and hung the pot of potatoes on the crook. "As soon as dinner is over I'll ask her," she told herself firmly.

Sunday afternoon was the only day Maggie sat down for any length of time, despite her seventy-seven years. "The devil makes work for idle hands" she often told her family, and set them a good example herself; apart from Sunday afternoons.

It was easy enough to find a husband for her youngest daughter, Alice, but Mary proved more difficult. "I wouldn't have bothered marrying at all myself, if my brother hadn't brought that sharp tartar of a wife of his into the house" she often told Mary.

"You are in a much better position than I was, this place will be yours when I go anyway," but despite these platitudes, Mary wanted a husband and family of her own before she was too old.

Then along came Johnny. It wasn't romantic love, but he was kind and generous and these two qualities had won her heart. Like all brides, Mary wanted to look her best on her wedding day, but without money to have a new frock made, and buy matching accessories, she had little hope.

The dishes washed, she sat down at the fire opposite her mother. "I was thinking about what

I'm going to wear to the wedding," she ventured looking wishfully at the old woman. "Well I've been giving that a bit of thought myself, so I asked Paddy to help me get my trunk down from the loft tomorrow."
Mary looked into the fire, her hopes fading. She could smell the must at the mere mention of that famous old trunk. "My wedding frock is still in there," she continued, "and I bet you a shilling it will look fine with a wash and a few repairs."
"The moths will have feasted on that old frock long ago mother," Mary debated, "I need a new one." But she knew by Maggie's actions that she didn't have a hope. "What good would a fancy frock be to you when the wedding is over? You are marrying a farmer, not a city gent!" she scorned. Mary then knew that she would have to resign herself to the fate that lay within the musty trunk.

Mary was walking across the yard carrying two buckets of milk when she saw Sally coming in the gate. "Lovely spring morning, thanks be to God!" Sally cheerfully called. "It takes yourself to get the milking done early. Johnny's a lucky man, he is indeed, to be marrying a grand worker." Mary laughed. 'Might as well laugh as cry,' she thought. Good worker was the only attribute Sally was ever going to credit her with.
They both walked into the kitchen to be greeted by

Maggie as she dusted the old trunk, which was sitting in the middle of the floor. Mary hoped her mother would keep the lid closed until Sally had gone, for if she caught sight of the moulding contents, it would surely be around the neighbourhood by nightfall. As luck would have it, Paddy, the servant boy, came in for his morning tea and Maggie busied herself getting it ready for him. Time was money to her, and the young scamp would waste time if he could. Paddy finished his tea and it took just a few acrid glances from Maggie to send him scurrying to the field again!

"Are you packing your trunk Maggie?" Sally inquired, her nose bothering her. "No" said Maggie, "I'm just about to sort out the table linen for the wedding."

"Oh, is that what you're doing Maggie?"

To Mary's horror, her mother ceremoniously opened the trunk, the smell of must greeting their nostrils. Out came the table linen. It looked yellow and moth-eaten as Maggie shook it out for inspection. The folds were brown. "When these have had a wash, the sun will bleach them," Maggie explained, undeterred. "The sun will have its work cut out," Mary muttered out of earshot. Mary sighed and left to put the cows out, she could stand no more.

While the table linen bleached on the whin-bushes,

Hazel McIntyre

Maggie spent all her spare time repairing the havoc the ravages of time had done to her frock. She covered the skirt with lace, her old fingers worked with nimble expertise. She was a clever needle woman.

Mary noticed the old dress finally washed and laying in state on the hill; the sun beaming down on it. She decided against having a closer inspection, telling herself she would have to see it soon enough.

Meanwhile Maggie had resurrected her funeral bonnet and was busy stripping the black silk until only the original yellow straw remained. She carefully cut the old lace to size and spent hours re-covering it. When it was finished, Maggie viewed it with satisfaction, but it lacked something! A yellow ribbon around the brim would be the very thing to finish it off she decided. One and a half yards should be enough she nodded to herself.

Wednesday morning dawned, bright and clear, it was Maggie's day for taking the eggs to the village. She hummed to herself as she cleaned the last two eggs. Six-dozen, all but one, then she heard the welcome sound from the hen-house. She had her six-dozen! Things were really going her way!

She stood in the shop holding her bag of eggs. Mrs Murphy had just ordered a quarter stone of rice. While the shopkeeper was weighing her order, she turned to Maggie. "The rice is very filling and nourishing for the children" she explained. Now Maggie knew that this woman had ten mouths to feed and the rice had to be economical. In a flash she had the answer to the catering dilemma for the wedding! When her eggs were counted and paid for, she ordered half a stone of rice, just to be on the safe side. She then asked for a yard and a half of ribbon. "How much is a yard?" "Three pence" the shopkeeper replied. She mentally calculated four pence halfpenny. Not too bad, she told herself. It's my only expenditure on the outfit.

Sarah, the bridesmaid, arrived on the eve of the wedding carrying her frock and hat in a brown paper bag. Tea over, she asked Mary to show her the wedding frock but before she could answer, Maggie went to the upper room and came back with a frock over her arm and a hat in the other hand.
 "Oh Lord, it looks lovely Mary" Sarah said, in astonishment. This was Mary's first close-up look at it since it emerged from the trunk. On closer inspection, she was amazed at the transformation. As for the funeral bonnet, it was a miracle. "Try it on Mary," Sarah enthusiastically urged.
Mary emerged from the room with hesitant steps, dressed in frock and hat. "It looks grand, Mary," Sarah cried. "Turn around, it's just perfect," she

nodded. "Are you telling me the truth Sarah?" Mary asked. "Honest, it's lovely," she replied taking the mirror from the wall and propping it against the leg of the table. As she stared at her reflection she whispered to herself, 'How did she do it? It really does look good.'

Maggie sat in silence watching them. At last she spoke. "I told you I'd made a good job of it," her laugh, a piercing crow of triumph.

The sun was just rising as Maggie got up. A thin mist hung low under the hills and the sound of bird-song filled the morning air, but Maggie had not time to admire the view, as she rushed out for the turf basket. "Not a neighbour up yet," she tutted, glancing around the townland chimneys for signs of turf smoke. "I hope Sally comes up early to give me a hand," she continued to herself. In the upper room, Mary had just got out of her bed, her rag curlers dangled around her face. "I'll do your hair for you in a minute," Sarah said sleepily. "There's plenty of time! the coach won't be here until half ten," Mary assured her.

Two hours later the bride and bridesmaid emerged from Mary's room dressed in their finery. "Well now, aren't you both a sight for sore eyes!" Sally greeted them. "You look every inch the lovely bride, you do indeed!" she continued.

"The coach is coming up the Shoeing-stone brae,"
Paddy called from the door.

The neighbours gathered to wave them off. They
were amazed at how well the bride looked, having
heard about her having to wear Maggie's old frock.
In the kitchen, Maggie carved the ham in thin
slices, and carefully laid it on the platter. She then
carefully laid the fancy pastries out on the best tray.
Sally watched her from the hearth where she was
frying the potato bread. How, she wondered,
would she feed thirty or so people on these small
quantities? Her question was answered as she
watched the old woman pour the dry rice into the
huge pot of hot water. Sally helped her cover the
long table in the lower room with white linen. The
brown patches that the sun wasn't able to bleach
were cunningly covered up with a butter dish or a
sugar bowl.

"Come quick, the rice is boiling over!" Paddy
shouted excitedly from the kitchen. Maggie ran to
the kitchen just as the rice was foaming and
bubbling out over the top of the pot. It sizzled on
the hot coals and landed on the floor. "Get me a
quart-pan quick," she shouted, "and bring me
another pot." She carefully transferred a quarter of
the rice into the other pot then added more water.
That done, she quickly scooped the spilled rice into

a bucket, "Take that out to the pigs Paddy!" she ordered. Paddy shook his head, "waste not, want not," he muttered banging the bucket on the door as he went. Maggie looked at the clock. "They should be back any minute now," she commented. "Paddy, run down to the end of the lane and turn the coach there, they can walk up that bit on this lovely day and anyway we don't need to feed the drivers!" she concluded, nodding.

The wedding guests were all seated at the table. "This is for starters," she said smiling as she placed a large bowl of rice in front of each of them. They looked at each other in astonished silence. Then the groom picked up his spoon and began to eat.
The first course over, Maggie placed the large platter of thinly cut ham in the middle of the table. Sally put the potato bread beside it. Then came the fancy pastries. Placing them on the sideboard she said in a coaxing voice, "now help yourselves to everything."
Feeling so bloated from the rice, they could only manage the merest morsels of the appetising array of fancy goodies before them.
Maggie left the dinner with a smile on her face. The neighbours arrived at the same time as the fiddle player and the celebrations really began in earnest. Between the jigs and reels, Maggie continued serving her generous portions of rice,

followed by the long lasting delicacies.

Maggie eased her tired body into her feather bed, just as the birds were beginning their dawn chorus. A broad smile crossed her old face, 'Well, they won't have it to say that they went hungry, and Mary looked well too.' She stifled a yawn and turned over, 'and it was all achieved at so little cost,' she reassured herself with satisfaction, as she fell into a deep sleep.

Aunt Bea closed the trunk, straightened, smoothed her apron and smiled, before she spoke again. "The story of Mary's wedding was all around 'The Nine Glens.' She was an example to all on economic wedding catering and a bridal outfit for fourpence-halfpenny."
Outside the rain had stopped and their earlier disappointments had vanished. "Didn't want to go to a silly old wedding anyway," John said, as they ran arm in arm down the laneway that led to the shore.

Easy Money
in the Modern World

The bar was quiet for a Friday evening. Dan sat down on his usual stool and glanced about him. 'Not a local in sight, just a clatter of strangers,' he muttered mournfully, as he ordered his pint of stout.

His attention was drawn to the conversation of the group of tourists sitting behind him as they discussed the cost of self-catering holiday cottages.

Echoes of Another Time

He whistled under his breath when he heard them mention the actual price of renting them. 'A body could live nicely all winter if they had one of them holiday places to rent out,' he said to himself.

The holiday rental business was still going round in his head the following morning, as he stood on the doorstep of his bungalow surveying his kingdom. As he looked out towards the Atlantic a grand thought occurred to him.

Swinging around he looked at the place with new vision, "It's a bit dilapidated. But, with a bit of paper an' paint it might just do the job," he said aloud. "Aye, it might just do the job."

With the help of his sister who lived nearby, his home was painted, papered and cleaned, transforming it almost out of recognition. Immediately after he advertised the place for rent, he got a reply from a family in San Diego, a couple and their two teenage daughters. They were in search of their roots and needed a place for the entire summer. Dan rubbed his hands together with delight when the deposit arrived in the post. He moved in with his sister temporarily and waited.

Just to be hospitable he left the Yanks a few bags of turf and a bag of his choice new spuds. They thanked him kindly, and he closed his ears to the teenage girls' shrill voices coming from within, complaining about only one bathroom, no shower and only two TV stations.

"How many bathrooms do they need for God's sake?" he muttered as he left them to settle in.

During the coming days and weeks he saw the couple out walking alone in the evenings. One evening he ventured to ask them why the daughters didn't join them for the walk, "oh, you know what teenage girls are like Danny. All they think about is…boys, boys, boys."

Dan wondered why they weren't keeping a closer eye on them, if they were that boy crazy. But he said nothing.

Soon the summer was over and time for the visitors to bid Dan a fond farewell. The girls kissed him on the cheek as Daddy handed over the final payment, leaving a relieved Dan to settle back into his home again.

A couple of weeks later Dan picked up his post from the mat. There was the usual junk mail, the phone bill, and a colourful postcard with a picture of California on it. He read.- *'We arrived back safely in San Diego and are settling back into the old routine. We had a grand time in dear old Ireland. Thank you again for your hospitality.'* As he read the P.S. at the bottom the sweat broke out on his brow and his legs turned to jelly. *'Thank you Danny boy for letting the girls have free use of your telephone point. It meant they were able to use their laptop computer to keep in touch all day long with their boyfriends back home in San Diego.'*

He tore open the Telecom Eireann bill and read; - four-hundred and fifty-six pounds fourteen pence.

The Confirmation Class

A long pale beam of spring sunlight slanted through the window lighting up the world map on the far wall. Daydreams of faraway places were interrupted by the schoolmaster's loud angry voice, then flinging his arms heaven-wards, with a gesture that had no roots in the classroom or the fearful looks on the faces of the confirmation class in progress. With an air of desperation, he lit a cigarette, which

he had unearthed from the thick hair round his ear.
"How in the name of the Lord above, you lot of numskulls will ever be well enough instructed for your confirmation, I don't know! I just don't know," he repeated, resting his head between his hands. As the only Protestant in the classroom I felt a sense of relief at not being expected to take part in the confirmation class, judging by his volatile mood. My attention was given to the lesson in progress, even though I had been given enough long division sums to keep me occupied for the duration.

A silent pause was followed by a gentle tapping on the classroom door. As the door was opened we heard him say "good afternoon Father," the cheerful voice far removed from the anger and despair portrayed a moment earlier. As the Priest entered the room we stood up and greeted him respectfully. He was a small, elderly man with a gentle face and soft brown eyes. He talked to the schoolmaster in quiet whispers before he addressed the class. "As you know confirmation is only three weeks away. I have come to see how your religious knowledge is progressing." With that he began asking questions, pointing at each student to indicate which one he was directing the question at. He nodded silently at each correct answer, and shook his head slowly at the incorrect ones. Soon his gaze fell on me. I knew the answers to the questions, as it had come up just prior to the Priest's arrival, I could mentally feel the pain that wee Joe must have felt when his earlobe was stretched like an elastic band because he gave the wrong answer. But instead of giving him the answer I stared back at him vacantly, and I breathed a sigh of relief when he moved the question on to someone else. But my relief was short lived. Looking at me again he asked another question. Staring back at him bewildered and unsure of myself, I remained silent yet again. A look of annoyance crossed his normally placid face. Then with a shake of his head he asked, in exasperation, "do you know nothing?"

At this point the schoolmaster cleared his throat loudly and whispered in his ear. Looking back at me he smiled and nodded in my direction with an air of apology.

We left the school and walked in silence through the rain. Joe walked on ahead, hunching his shoulders against the storm and rubbing his earlobe periodically. "I should have answered the questions," I said absently.

"What questions?"

"The ones the Priest asked me."

"But you weren't supposed to know."

"Maybe not. But I knew the answers, and I felt an idiot."

"You're lucky that you don't need to know the catechism."

"But when it's my turn for confirmation, I'll have to

walk to Culdaff for the lessons after school."

"Whatever teacher you have, couldn't surely be as bad as him," she said nodding back in the direction of the school.

Confirmation day came and went, and shortly afterwards the summer holidays freed us all from the confines of the schoolroom. Just before the return to school in September, a neighbour died suddenly, casting gloom in the neighbourhood.

October flamed with coloured leaves, and the wayside ferns turned colours of golds and rusts. Then came a day of wind and driving rain, leaving the trees bare in its wake.

It was my turn to keep the recently bereaved widow company.

We sat at either side of the fire in silence amid the dark advance of an already gloomy afternoon, when we heard the gentle tapping at the door. I answered it with a sense of relief, at the possibility of an early escape. The Priest stood in the doorway. "Hello Father." He smiled back at me vacantly at first, then slowly into his eyes came a light of recognition. "Now I remember you," he said. "I'm sorry about asking you the questions. And then scolding you," he added, with a slow shake of his head.

"But, I knew the answers. I thought that I wasn't supposed to answer, you see," with a chuckle, he reached down and ruffled my hair. "You are a grand girl. And thank you for keeping Mary in company at this sad time."

I skipped back down the lane, feeling both relieved to be released from the sadness of Mary's house and at having let the Priest know that I wasn't stupid after all.

Later studies for my own confirmation proved that the religious knowledge I had acquired accidentally came in very useful. Protestant sins and punishments were just as much to be feared as Roman Catholic ones, I found out.

The Homecoming

Grace stood silently gazing after the

disappearing bus on a wet, late autumn evening, then picking up her bags, turned and walked up the hill into the semi-twilight.

Rounding the bend in the narrow lane she felt the same quiver of fear she had known as a youngster in fear of the dark shadows. Standing for a moment to rest, a surge of joy at the familiarity of it all came over her. A streak of blue in the sky was clouding over. The hills looked dark and haunting, and she could hear the distant roll of the sea. Grace was a small, slim, smartly dressed woman with vivid blue eyes and auburn hair tinged with grey.

Twenty-five years had passed since she last set eyes on this once familiar scene as a sixteen-year-old with a head full of hopeful dreams of faraway places, where life would be easy and where she would be freed from the confines of a small rural community.

Her thoughts went back to her long years in a Boston suburb; the initial daily grind of the clothing factory and the lonely evenings of her drab apartment, a far cry from the free and easy life of her dreams.

Then she met John, the man she had adored. The years following her marriage had been happy, affluent ones, days of wine and roses that came to an end when he was killed in a train crash.

Later, there had been other men in her life, but none had measured up to her first love.

Her decision to return home had been a sudden one, so sudden that she could scarcely believe that she was here at all. She had managed to shut out thoughts of home for years, and the letter writing had ceased after her mother's death eleven years ago. Her father could not forgive her for running away from home and her letters had remained unanswered.

Yet, this sudden and overwhelming desire to return had taken possession of her, like a command that had to be obeyed.

Her thoughts went back to her growing years and how she had yearned to be freed from the endless toil of farm-work. The eldest of seven siblings, the responsibilities had weighed heavily on her young shoulders.

She had planned her escape carefully, saving every penny that came her way. A stroke of good fortune made it all possible, when she had been rewarded for taking care of a sick neighbour; her nephew had handed her two pounds on the day of her funeral.

A strict Baptist, her father had been a stern man and a strong disciplinarian who talked constantly about the sin of pride. He was most anxious, as he said that Grace should not get above herself. And yet her memories were bittersweet. Standing still in the near darkness she could remember her parents, brothers, sisters, friends, the winters and the summers, the young and the dead, the snow, the rain and the dancing.

She remembered sneaking out at night to the village dances and even now all these years on, she could remember her dread of the consequences of her father finding out. Simple stolen pleasures such as this were to be savoured and treasured because there wasn't all that much fun to be had back then. But even this simple pleasure was to come to an abrupt end when a neighbour innocently divulged her secret. She had been beaten by her father, and confined to the house like a prisoner. It was then she planned her escape.

The memory of her going on a chilly dawn, tears streaming down her face, carrying a small shabby suitcase came back clearly to her now.
How young and naive she had been, and how little she had known of the world that awaited her and of how much she would miss them all.
Then a rush of joy ran through her and she walked on. Turning into the narrow lane that led to the cottage that was once her home her stomach muscles began to tense and her throat became dry. Would anyone even remember her? That she might not be welcome had just occurred to her.

The front gate opened with a reluctant creak. Then lifting her hand she gave a sharp knock. A dog barked from deep within and a light appeared through the glass above the door. When the door opened a youngish dark haired woman stood there looking at her vacantly.
Then slowly a light of recognition came into Grace's eyes. She was looking at the sister she had last seen as a seven-year-old. "Are you Anna?"

Echoes of Another Time

The young woman nodded. "I'm your sister. I'm Grace. You won't remember me...but, I remember you."

Anna stood open mouthed for a few seconds before standing aside. "You better come in I suppose. He won't want you near the place you know...Daddy. He would never let us mention your name."

Inside the warm kitchen Grace looked around. It had been modernised and changed out of all recognition apart from the old wall clock, which began to hiss as it chimed the hour. Modern gadgets seemed somehow out of place; they belonged to that other world she had just left. "I want to go to bed," a female voice from the corner broke the poignant silence.

For the first time she saw the old woman sitting by the stove. She glanced at Anna with a puzzled expression. "It's Aunt Kate. Mammy's sister. She's a bit confused...you know, doting. I look after her now. There's nobody else," she added with a sigh. The old woman rose slowly from her chair and shuffled towards the door. Standing in the doorway, she scrutinised Grace doubtfully. "Who is she?" she asked not taking her eyes from Grace's face. "It's Grace. Your niece who's been away." "This hussy's not wee Grace."

There was a pause. Not taking her eyes from Grace's face, it seemed as though she was inviting her to speak.

"I am Grace. Don't you remember me?"

"Aye … I liked wee Grace. But I don't know you."
Turning away, she shuffled on out the door.

Anna took her arm and began to escort her towards
the hall. "I'll help her into bed and I'll make you
some tea."

Alone Grace wandered around the kitchen trying
desperately to recapture something from the past.
That she had been living in a time warp suddenly
seemed to dawn on her, she had somehow expected
everything to be the same, that the intervening
twenty-five years had never happened.

She felt the sharp pain of loneliness that she had
felt as she walked into exile a quarter of a century
earlier. She felt alienated in a strange place and was
about to walk back out into the darkness when
Anna opened the door again.

"Where are you going?" she asked glancing at the
suitcase in her hand.

"I've decided to leave. I don't belong anymore."

"Don't be daft. You've just got here. Sit down and
we'll talk while I make the tea." There was an
almost pleading look on Anna's face as she spoke.

"All right I'll stay for the tea." Putting her suitcase
down Grace removed her coat and sat down in the
armchair.

"I'll stay for a while then. But I know now I
shouldn't have come back.

It feels like I'm a ghost from another time…I just

don't belong here now."

Banging the teapot down on the stove, Anna turned to face her.

"What the hell did you expect? You come swaging back here after all these years expecting to be welcomed like some prodigal daughter. Not a letter, or a bloody thing from you for nearly a lifetime. I'm the one that gave up my life and my youth. First my mother, then Daddy and now Kate."

"Where did you get the idea that I didn't write?" Grace shouted back. "I sent hundreds of letters home to each and every one of you; I sent every spare dollar I could get for years. Mother was the only one that answered my letters, the only one."

A sound from the doorway made them turn around.

"Daddy, what are you doing out of bed?" Anna asked in a quiet voice.

Grace stared open mouthed at the stooped, shrunken figure leaning on a walking stick. The grey, baggy Aran sweater he wore hung loosely over his shrunken frame. The shock at the change in him sent her head reeling. Could this really be the big, strong self-assured man that she remembered?

"Grace has … come home to visit us. Come and sit down Daddy."

He shook his head. The blood mounted to his forehead and his eyes flashed. "Go back to wherever … you come from." His voice shook with emotion, then tapping his stick on the floor he turned to go. "Wait," Anna said, "I want you to tell me something. The truth mind, seeing as you're always preaching about the sin of lies. Did Grace here write letters home all down the years? Did she send money home to us?" Not turning around to face her, he muttered inaudibly. "Look at me and tell me the truth." Anna's voice shook as she spoke. He slowly turned around to face them. "Aye…she sent letters. Letters damned letters. Never read one of them. They're lying up in a drawer in the room. If you don't believe me … go, go and look," his voice trailed away.

"What are you talking about, didn't open them? Why in God's name didn't you tell me to open them? I want to know. I want to know now!" Her voice shook with emotion as she spoke. They stood in silence for a few moments, then Anna said in a softer tone. "Come and sit down Daddy. We must get this all out in the open." Her voice became sharper again. "Get up here now and talk." The redness left his face and he slowly made his way up to the chair near the range.

Seated in the chair opposite, Grace looked at him and as their eyes met she shuddered inwardly at the hostility she sensed in them. As she stared at his hewn features, to her surprise she experienced a homesickness for all that was past, a longing to see her mother again, her siblings around the turf fire, the harvest moon, the fiddle that her mother used to play to them when her father wasn't around. To her annoyance the tears began to come without warning.

Through the blur of her tears Anna stood looking down at her. "The letters. I found them at the back of the bottom drawer." She slumped down in a nearby chair and flicked through the bundle of unopened letters. "Some of these are over twenty years old," she muttered.

Then turning her gaze towards her father, she asked. "Why Daddy? Why? You hid these letters that were meant for my mother. You stole her letters and hid them. Look at me for fuck sake!"

"I won't have cursing in my house. Do you hear me?" He made to get to his feet, anger flaring in his eyes. The walking stick slipped sideways and he slumped back into the chair again.

"You're a hypocrite. Don't like cursing. I don't much like people who steal other people's letters either. Your halo's slipping Daddy," Anna said, glancing at him with a sarcastic grin.

"She ran out on us without a bye your leave. Can you imagine what the neighbours thought eh? Had to make up a concocted story about a sick relative who needed her more that us."

"The neighbours. The neighbours and your damned pride was more important than your daughter."

Grace felt a leaping nausea in her stomach,

dizziness behind her eyes as she listened to the angry exchange between her father and sister.

'I shouldn't have come back. I should have stayed away and remembered everything as it was,' she inwardly screamed.

With half-seeing eyes, she watched her father shuffle from the room.

"These are yours now," Anna said, getting up and handing her the bundle of yellowing letters.

Grace idly flicked through the letters that she had written years before. Then turning one over she opened it and began to read. At the end of the letter she had written 'I hope the enclosed $20 will help with Christmas.' She searched the envelope and then the floor for the dollar notes but found none.

"What are you looking for Grace?" Hanna asked with a frown.

"I sent twenty dollars to Mother for Christmas in this letter, but it's not there."

"Let me see," Hanna said, taking the letter from Grace's outstretched hand. Turning the envelope over she examined it carefully.

"Can I see the rest?"

When she had examined each letter thoroughly she looked back at Grace. "These letters have all been read. Steamed open. Look at the smudged glue and wrinkled paper" she added, showing the evidence to Grace.

He watched and listened from the doorway, "I

didn't open one of them. As I have my Maker to meet. I didn't open one of them," his voice, barely a whisper.

Turning around to look at him, Anna's face suddenly lit up. "Mother. She found your hiding place. She was always one step ahead … God bless her." Then with a shake of the head, she looked across at Grace, "That's why we didn't get to read ours. She was afraid we might let the cat out of the bag."

Their emotions were a mixture of pity and anger as they watched him shuffle from the room again. At the door he turned to face them. "I … I'm sorry. I should have been more forgiving." Then looking towards the ceiling he said, "I only hope she has forgiven me."

Presbyterian Cow

A weak wintry sun had just crept over the

horizon as Joe and Hanna made their way up the
hill to visit the returned 'Yankee'.

"First time home in twenty-five years," Joe had
said the night before.

"They say she has a whole suitcase full of candy."
This piece of news clinched it for Hanna. They
would go the following morning and welcome the
'Yankee' back home.

"Yanks in the movies drink coffee and Martinis,"
Joe announced as they neared the top of the hill.
"What is Martini like?"
"Poteen … well, a bit like Poteen," Joe replied, his
breath coming like bursts of mist in the frosty air.
"Hope she doesn't offer us any then. Daddy says
Poteen's only for sick cows … that's why he keeps
it."

The hall door was open when they reached the
house. They knocked and went in. When we were
introduced she stood up to greet us. She was tall
and was elegantly dressed in a fawn suit; she wore
red lipstick and red nail varnish. Bending down
she gave each in turn a big slobbery kiss.
'YUK!' Joe said inwardly, then made to wipe his
cheek. He thought of the candy and decided to
wait in case he upset her.
As Anna watched her sip black coffee and listened
to her strange sounding accent she wondered if she
really was a movie star after all.
Then came the moment they had been waiting for.
The 'Yankee' left the room and returned with the
candy, lots of it in brightly coloured packets.
As they were leaving she handed each of them a
small package. "Just a couple of trinkets to
remember me by," she drooled, planting another
kiss on each of their cheeks. This time Joe hastily
wiped his sloppy kiss away on his sleeve when

they were out of sight. Tearing open her small parcel Hanna uncovered a green necklace and bracelet, "Emeralds" she cried out in glee. That her emeralds were made of plastic mattered not a whit. "What did you get Joe?"
"A gun with bullets. Paper ones," he said, holding out the roll of paper caps.

They had munched their way though a pound of the 'Yankee' candy by the time they reached the home straight. Willy, their nearest neighbour was leading a red cow into the byre as they neared his farmyard. His wife Sara appeared from the back door of the cottage. "Andy's just bought another cow," she announced. They followed her into the byre, dimly lit by a hurricane lamp. "She looks a grand animal" she said, with pride. "I must bless her." She reached up to a shelf at the far corner and took down a bottle.
"Where did you buy her?" Joe inquired, as he put the last candy into his mouth.
"From Robert Johns. No, she wouldn't have had a drop of holy water on her before with that background," she added, as she liberally shook the liquid over the cow's back. Suddenly the cow began to jump, flinging her hind legs in the air. "Hold her Willy, the Presbyterian is very strong in her," she shouted above the commotion.
Retreating out of the flinging animal's way, John

grabbed the bottle from his wife and headed for the open door.

"Stupid woman," he shouted, "it's caustic soda you blessed her with."

The Patent Shoes

With her nose touching the window, while her breath created a ring of steam on the glass, Mary gazed for the fourth day on the trot at the objects of her heart's desire on display in Ryan's shop window. The rainbow coloured nylon net petticoat, and underneath lay the shiny black patent stiletto heeled shoes, made her heart ache with longing.

Echoes of Another Time

Walking back down the brae to school again, oblivious to the cold December sleet in the wind, she was lost in a world of make-belief. She saw herself dancing in the red dress, with the rainbow petticoat just visible underneath and on her feet the shiny black stilettos. But as the prohibitive prices loomed up, the daydream began to fade, the Cinderella image was back among the cinders again in a drab school gymslip.

On our way home in the bus that evening, we all felt a wonderful sense of freedom as we contemplated the two week Christmas holidays. Mary glanced once again at the shoes and petticoat as the bus passed the window. Sitting on the seat beside her, Hanna asked, "Did you manage to get any more money saved yet?"
"Just three shillings. I still need two pounds."
"Only eight days left 'till the Ballyliffen dance," she reminded her friend.

In the kitchen her mother was making Christmas pudding. "I'm home. Any letters?" she asked, throwing her bag to the ground.
"There's a letter for you on the mantle shelf. Christmas card I think," she said, not taking her eyes from her work. The card was from her older sister in London, and tucked inside, joy of joy, was a crisp pound note. Holding it to her heart she

whispered "thank you." She was now only one pound short; the shoes and petticoat almost within reach. Looking across at her mother as she took a tray of golden brown buns from the range oven, she judged now to be as good a time as any to ask for the other pound.

"I got a pound from Liz for Christmas," she began. "But I need another pound to buy the shoes and petticoat I want."

Her mother was bent over the oven putting another batch of buns inside. Now she straightened and faced her. "What kind of shoes?" she asked.

"Oh, they're lovely. Black patent … stilettos."

"Stilettos! School shoes would be far more sensible," her mother said disapprovingly.

"Please. I have always wanted a pair of stilettos," she pleaded. "I will do any jobs you want; anything."

She saw her face soften before she said, "Oh, all right. It is Christmas I suppose."

Walking over to where her mother stood, Mary kissed her on the cheek, feeling a surge of triumph sweep over her.

The shop was crowded with Saturday night shoppers when she went in. When her turn came to be served she asked for a pair of the shoes that were on display in the window.

"What size?"

"Five."

A couple of minutes later she came back with the shoes in a white box. "You better try them on." Taking the right shoe from the box, she handed it to Mary. It fitted perfectly. "They're fine," she answered happily. "Better try the other one," the assistant advised.

"No need. Don't want to miss the bus," she added, handing over the two pounds.

Friday night came at last. By nine o'clock Mary was putting the finishing touches to her make-up when Hanna arrived dressed and ready for the dance. Giving the new shoes another admiring glance she slipped her feet into them. It took a few seconds before the terrible reality dawned; one shoe felt bigger than the other.

"Oh Lord, Hanna, I'll never be able to jive in these shoes. The left one feels far too big." She wailed. "Take them off and let me see." Then turning them upside down she said. "I can see the problem. One is a size five and the other is six and a half. You'll have to take them back and change them."

"What good is that. I need them now," Mary said close to tears. Glancing at the shoe-box, Hanna seized on an idea. Grabbing the tissue paper from the box, she said, "Here, shove this in the toe of the big shoe," Mary grinned at her through the tears, "You're a lifesaver Hanna," she said, as she stuffed the tissue inside the shoe that was a size and a half too big for her.

The dance hall was all aglow with glittering light when they arrived, paper chains and balloons hung in festive grandeur from every nook and cranny. When Mary and Hanna made their grand entrance they cast a professional eye over the opposite sex standing in rows at the far side of the hall. For Mary one lad stood out from the rest; his raven black hair was slicked back from his face, and the long sideburns gave him more than a passing resemblance to Elvis Presley.

When the old time waltz finished, the band exchanged their squeeze boxes for guitars and began to play rock 'n' roll. Mary beamed with delight when the Elvis look-a-like came over and asked her to jive. They were jiving at great speed to 'Jailhouse Rock' when it happened.

The big shoe left her foot, went flying through the air and landed on the head of the guitar player. Mary watched in horror, then looked the other way, hoping that no one would notice where the shoe came from. Then to her deep embarrassment she heard a voice over the microphone loudly announce: "Will the blonde girl in the red dress come up to the stage for her shoe."

Mary could feel her face blaze red with embarrassment as she made a lopsided move to the stage. As the young guitar player held out her shoe, she could see the white tissue paper hanging out in long crumpled strips. Glancing back at her dance partner, she noticed that his face glistened with a greasy sheen from melted Brylcream, while his previously sleeked black raven hair was now nothing more than greasy black strings; the Elvis image completely vanished. She hastily thanked him for the dance, and walked back, shoe in hand to make herself as invisible as possible behind a row of girls standing at the side of the hall. Suddenly she felt a tap on her shoulder, she looked up to meet the eyes of the guitar player.

"Will you dance?" he asked with a smile.

She flushed in spite of herself, all her nerves tingling. The band played 'I'm Dreaming of a White Christmas,' while they danced cheek to cheek. When the dance ended he said: "I need a breath of fresh air. Will you come with me?"

Mary nodded, then went to get her coat. As they walked hand in hand into the cold frosty air, and away from the noisy dance hall, he asked: "Will you tell me why you had papers stuffed in your shoe?"

When she finished telling him, his laughter echoed in the silent frosty air. "Don't laugh at me. It was very embarrassing, at the time," she said with a chuckle. Then bending down he kissed her gently on the lips; while faintly in the distance the band played the National Anthem. Looking up at the bright stars Mary decided that this must surely be love.

Satin Frocks and Missions

With the cream satin material secured on the parcel-carrier Hanna, set off for the dressmaker with a clear picture in her head of the finished garment. A shift dress, with a square neck and a pencil slim skirt just above the knee.

The coming summer stretched out ahead with all its promise of good times, and she felt a mounting excitement at thoughts of her sisters and city friend returning for the annual holiday and the dances.

Mary the dressmaker was tall and stout, with a laugh fit to split your eardrums and an unceasing flow of chatter about the neighbours, the weather and the wicked cost of everything in the shops. "Let's get comfortable she would say." Then she would smooth down the reddish-grey frizz of hair, and let out her great laugh and plump down in her favourite easy-chair. Hanna would wait patiently for Mary to complete her ritual so she would have her undivided attention.

"Now what would you like me to create for you this time?"

Mary nodded periodically while Hanna explained how she wanted her new dress to look.

"Right then, let's get the measuring done. And I'll be ready for a fitting by Friday."

On the way home she met two of her school friends. "Where were you?" she asked, noting their smart attire.

"The mission's on. Started tonight. A whole week of morning and evening." Josephine replied.

"Good job you're a Protestant."

"Where were you?" her sister Margaret asked.

"Down with Mary to get a new frock made."

"If you'd been to the mission and heard the Holy Father's sermon on sin, and Hell an' the sin of vanity, you wouldn't be thinking about new frocks."

Echoes of Another Time

When Josephine had finished reliving the sermon, Hanna's mind was far away from the new shift-style frock, instead she expected to see the Devil himself, appearing from behind every whin-bush they passed.

"We have missions too sometimes. They preach much the same sort of stuff," Hanna said, with a note of sympathy.

Half way up the steep brae, Margaret suggested they visit her uncle Joe.

Joe's kitchen was warm and inviting and he soon had a cup of steaming coca for each of them.

The talk soon became centred on the mission and Josephine went over the details of the sermon once more.

Joe poked the fire and put on a few more turf before lighting his pipe.

"There was a mission once when I was a wee fellow. Anyway, we were all sent to the church from school one day and seated in the front pews. The Holy Father in his wisdom decided to warn us about the evils of drink. He was well prepared - for he had two glasses with him, one with water in it and one with whiskey in it. Then he took a worm from a matchbox and put it into the glass with the water. Well, the worm was wriggling about in the water nice as you like. The Priest held up the glass for us all to see. 'Now,' says he, 'look at how well the worm does in God's good clear water.'"

A smile crossed Joe's face before he went on, "Well, then he put the worm into the whiskey glass - and it just shrivelled up and died. Looking down at us he asked, 'Now children - what does that tell you about whiskey?'
Well, wee Andy's hand shot up in the air. 'Excuse me Father,' says he, 'That tells you that if you have worms - drink plenty of whiskey.'"

When we left Joe's our spirits had lifted and Hanna's thoughts were back, once more, on summer fun and new frocks.

Mary was seated in front of the big Singer sewing machine when Hanna went in. She waited patiently until she had finished the hem she was sewing. Then swinging around to face Hanna, she said, "Well your frock is finished. Come and try it on."
"Well what do you think of it?"
"It's perfect. Just what I wanted," Hanna said, eyeing herself in the long mirror on the wardrobe door.
Later at home she tried on the new dress again to show it to her sisters, who had just arrived home for the holidays. They were impressed.
"It's just as fashionable as the London designers' new collections," Liz announced.
Just a week later Mary had made two more shift dresses exactly the same as Hanna's.

Echoes of Another Time

It was raining hard on the night of the parochial dance, and rather than risk getting the new dresses wet, it was decided that they should carry them in a bag and dress in the cloakroom.

They stood in a row in their cream satin, slim-line frocks and saw the admiring glances of their friends.

As the first on the floor, it only took seconds for Hanna to discover the problem. The pencil skirt had imprisoned her leg movements to steps of just a couple of inches. After a few minutes of frantic struggle, she glanced at her puzzled partner, "a stone in my foot," she muttered in desperation.

In the cloakroom she had only a few minutes to wait until her red-faced sisters joined her. "I've never been so mortified," they exclaimed almost in unison, their grand entrance just an embarrassing memory.

With a wintry wee smile they left, walked slowly out of the hall - shuffling slightly. Outside, Hanna looked at the darkened church and in her head she could hear the sermon about the sin of pride and how it always comes before a fall.

Summer Rain and Jimmy Shand

The evening air was warm and humid, their starched petticoats swinging like kites as they set out to walk the two miles to the dance.

Suddenly, the sky darkened and the rain followed with unexpected swiftness.

Taking to their heels, they dived into Robby's roadside cottage in a desperate bid for shelter. He sat alone in his fire-side chair, barely glancing at their breathless and unexpected entrance.

"Can we take shelter here 'till the rain stops?" Hanna asked, her breath coming in short bursts. He nodded without turning his head. "Can we dry ourselves at the fire?" Mary ventured. Again a slight nod.

He poked the fire and added a few whin-sticks between the turf and it leaped into flames. Robby's abode was new to the three girls. He was locally known as a bit of an oddball. 'Dry oul' stick.' 'Wouldn't know what to make of him.' 'Doesn't want anybody about the place,' were the local comments.

But they were desperate to get out of the rain and so they had no option but to stay put until the rain stopped.

In the uncomfortable silence they watched him light his pipe and lie back in the chair, his bright blue eyes lost amongst the black rafters of the ceiling.

Hanna cleared her throat noisily, "How long do you think the rain will last?" she ventured.

Getting up, he went to the window and looked out. Without a word, he went back to his chair and sat down. Then he spoke for the first time.

"Don't know why you didn't invest in one of them plastic Mackintoshes. Hoods an' all on them. They are only about half a crown and they fold up to fit

in a wee bag. Aye, don't know why. A climate like
ours is the place for them - aye, the place for
plastic covering."

The sound of his voice and his knowledge of
plastic coats stunned them into momentary silence.
"How do you know about plastic coats?" Mary
asked.

"The catalogue. Get it every month." Then getting
to his feet he switched on the light and reached up
to a shelf at the side of the fireplace. "The stuff
about the plastic coats is on page fifty six."

Hanna saw it first, on a shelf on the far wall beside
the wireless.

"Is that a record player?" she asked, in amazement.
"Aye," Robby said, "it's the latest model. You can
put on four or five LP's at a time. Do you want to
see how it works?" he asked, with an air of pride
and a sprightliness that belied his earlier pose.
They stood in a row, admiring this feat of modern
technology found in such an unexpected place. As
she watched Robby demonstrate this modern
wonder, Hanna's thoughts went back to the old
gramophone, and the new, vinyl record of Buddy
Holly, that she had to watch in dismay as it peeled
in loops in the wake of the needle.

From under the shelf he took a small bundle of
records, which he inspected with a touch of anxiety
as if he feared mice had been nibbling at them in

his absence.

The first record dropped onto the turntable and the kitchen resounded to Scottish dance music. "Jimmy Shand," he shouted, above the noise.

"Have you any Elvis records?" Hanna shouted.

"Not a one. That oul' music is not my style," he shouted back, with a determined shake of the head. The next tune slowed to a waltz. "Can any of you dance a waltz, or is it all that rock 'n' roll stuff you do?"

"I'll waltz with you" Mary said, going over to the middle of the floor.

He hesitated for a minute. "Right then. Right you are," he said, rubbing his hands on his trouser legs, before crossing the floor to join her. They stumbled awkwardly for a moment before getting into step. Robby's face lit up in sheer pleasure as they waltzed around the flag floor in perfect step to the music.

Above the noise of the music a loud rattle sounded outside. Looking flustered, he stopped the dance. "God, who could that be?" he asked, a look of utter confusion on his face. "I forgot, it's Mick's night for the groceries."

"A lift. He might give us a lift in the lorry," Hanna said, with a broad grin.

They emerged from the back of Mick's lorry, with their skirts still swinging and a liberal dusting of white flour from the lorry floor clinging to their lace petticoats.

In the shelter of the dance-hall porch they began beating the flour out of their petticoats with their hands, the white flour rising up around them like an eerie summer mist. "Powdering your noses girls?" a male voice asked from the open doorway. They could hear his mocking laughter still echoing long after he'd gone.

"I'm mortified," Hanna wailed.

"I'm going back to Robby's for the address of that place for the plastic Mac's," Kate's voice came out of the floury mist.

They danced the night away surrounded by a white dusty halo.

In Memory of an Animal Lover

Andy's corpse was laid out in the parlour surrounded by his neighbours when we arrived at the house. Nobody spoke, just the occasional cough and shuffle of feet broke the eerie silence. Paddy Murphy sat at the head of the coffin gazing into space as he stroked his pipe between his fingers. Apart from us, Paddy knew Andy better than any of them. He put up with Andy's mood swings and bad temper; he was the only one who really knew the man that lay underneath the bad tongue he was famous for.

He saw himself again just a couple of days ago on a drizzly afternoon helping Andy to cover the potato pit. Little did he know then that he would never clap eyes on him alive again. "Died in his sleep," the doctor told him, "heart attack."

Patch, his brown spaniel sat in the doorway with a sorrowful expression in his soulful eyes. We remembered well the day Andy brought the wee dog home. He told him how he had seen him running along the road at a full stretch gallop, head extended forward as though in desperate pursuit of something unseen beyond the long stretch of empty road ahead. Andy had seen something chilling there, a momentary but vivid impression of frantic effort, despair and blind terror.

He cycled after the dog and found him lying exhausted a bit further up the road. As he was examining the dog a car engine sounded and he watched the wide panting mouth close and his whole body stiffen as the car approached. For a moment the dog stared at it with fierce hope but when the vehicle flashed by he sagged and began to pant again. So that was it. He had been dumped. "I could forgive anybody for robbing a bank. But not for this," he told us that evening.

"The humans he had loved and trusted, opened their car door, hurled him out and drove away."

Echoes of Another Time

That was how Andy was when it came to animals. He carried the wee dog home and gradually restored his trust in human kind with the affection and loyalty he showed him. He often told us how, each time Patch heard a car pass he would prick up his ears, stiffen his back with hope that his former owners had returned to claim him.

Andy had rescued a young donkey with overgrown hooves from a man he met at a fair. "Had to pay ten pounds for him. He had half starved the poor animal - it was the only way to get him out of his clutches."
Children and animals brought out the best in Andy.

Hanna nudged me when Paddy got up to go and we followed him outside.
"When's the funeral?" Johnny asked, as we made our way down the narrow lane.
"Not 'till Thursday. Seems some nephew in America is flying over for the funeral. Looking for a share of the farm. Nothing changes. Never even visited him when he was living."
"What's going to happen to Patch?" Hanna asked.
He stopped suddenly in his tracks. "I clean forgot. Must go back for him," he added, turning on his heel heading back towards the wake house.
Patch lay on the doorstep and wagged his tail as we approached. "Come on Patch. Come home with me." The dog looked up at him soulfully but didn't

move. "Nothing here for you now. He won't be back," he added bending down to pick up the dog. We walked back down the lane in silence, Paddy carrying the wee dog.

The following evening we went back to the wake house and were greeted at the door by the Yankee nephew. "How good of you to come," he drooled sweetly as he led the way into the parlour.
Once seated he continued talking. "It's so good to see all Uncle Andy's friends and neighbours. True friends until the end," he added, with a mournful shake of the head.

We followed Andy's funeral procession on foot. Michael, the Yankee nephew helped to carry the coffin down the rutted lane-way to where the hearse waited. As the coffin was loaded the donkey began a long ear piercing 'heeeee haw…. heee haw.'
The sorrowful sound filled the silent, still air like a lament.

When the funeral was over we walked home with Paddy.
"Will that nephew get everything?" Hanna asked, as though reading our thoughts.
"Aye, in a way," Paddy replied, a broad grin forming on his face.

"What do you mean in a way?"

"You'll find out soon enough. Aye, you'll find out soon enough."

"Ah, go on - tell us," Hanna persisted.

His eyes glanced away towards the darkening hills and his brows knitted, as if the explanation was beyond his ability to describe.

"Well, he left the place to Michael, the Yankee. But, two fields go to the donkey - grazing for his lifetime. So you see, he can't sell it as long as the donkey lives. He's only a young donkey, an' could live twenty or more years."

Echoes

Ignoring the pouring rain, Lawrence walked down the busy, wet London street, his mind on food and warmth. Suddenly, a voice from a passer-by grabbed his attention. He recognised that voice, it was very familiar, and yet he couldn't for the moment put a name or a face to it.

Turning around he walked swiftly back in the opposite direction searching the bent heads of the crowds waiting in bus queues. He followed a group of people into the tube-station; listening and watching like someone possessed. As he stood there, rain-water dripping down his neck from the collar of his duffel coat, he felt foolish as he listened to the hub of voices all around him.

He was about to leave when a figure turned around from one of the ticket booths. He had been right - it was she! "Mary. Mary Gillespie," he shouted, going over to where she stood. Her expression was blank as she stared in his direction. "Don't you remember me? Lawrence. Lawrence McKay." To his immense relief, into her eyes came a light of recognition and a broad smile lit up her face. "You look great. As beautiful as ever."

"I don't feel very beautiful at this minute. I'm soaked," she said, flicking her fingers through her wet hair.

"Wet or not you look great. Could we meet up somewhere later?"

"Right. You name the venue. We have a lot to catch up on." The smile she directed at him brought him back to childhood. It took a minute or two for him to bring himself back from Donegal to the bustle of London, and when his mind was clear of it, he was left with an aching longing to go home.

Leaving Mary to catch her train, he walked back along the wet streets, his thoughts drifting back to childhood and the part that Mary had played in it.

When the schoolmaster left the room Lawrence tugged one of the pigtails of the girl in the desk in front of him. "We are going down to the glen for nuts on the way home. Want to come?"

"Right" she nodded, with a grin. "Did you take a bag to put them in?"

He shook his head. "We can use our school bags - leave the books at the end of the Port Road."

He hadn't heard the teacher's return until a sudden thud on the back of his head from behind made him jump. "That will teach you not to gossip when my back's turned," he bellowed.

When he moved to another pupil, Mary glanced back at him with sympathy in her eyes. He smiled back at her even though his head throbbed from the effects of the sudden blow.

Later the Parish Priest called at the school and talked about dying in a state of grace - an event that seemed so far ahead he could not envisage it. Lawrence feverishly hoped that eternity would be free of teachers with ready fists and sharp canes.

A week later Lawrence took sick. He felt hot and achy and had a thumping headache. Finally the rash appeared.

"Measles," his grandmother proclaimed. "You will have to stay in bed, and keep the curtains drawn to protect your eyes." At first he had felt too sick to care as he lay in a twilight world between sleeping and waking.

But as soon as he began to feel better he wanted to escape the darkened room. His grandmother was always there to halt his attempts to escape.

Looking back, he remembered her as a shrunken ball of energy, always dressed in black with a piece of knitting tucked into her apron pocket.

It was Mary who came to his rescue. He heard her voice from the kitchen one evening, "Can I go down and see Lawrence?" His mother's voice came back, "You better stay where you are if you don't want to get the measles." "I've had them already," came the cheery reply.

She came into the darkened room like a breath of summer carrying a bundle of books. "I can't read books without light" he told her sullenly. "Well, I'll tell you stories then."

The stories from Mary's imagination lifted his spirits and transported him away from the dim room to a world of exciting adventure. The main character in Mary's imaginary adventures was old Pat a neighbouring farmer, a thin wisp of a man who had spent his entire life in the same parish. Mary supplied him with an aeroplane, which he kept on the foreshore from where he flew to distant lands. His adventures were always heroic and his rescues daring. Lawrence smiled at the remembrance of Pat's great transformation from his mundane existence to a hero. Mary's vivid imagination turned Pat into yesterday's 'Superman.'

The journey to the hotel where he arranged to meet Mary was one of unashamed nostalgia for Lawrence. He became a child again as long buried memories of the growing years crowded into his head. The longing to go back and become that child that he once was, if only for a wee while filled his whole being.

Meeting Mary again after all these years had re-kindled in him feelings that he thought he had buried.

He had been waiting in the hotel foyer about five minutes when he saw her come through the door. They sat in a corner and talked until closing time. When it was time to go Lawrence asked to see her again. She looked at him with a wishful expression before she spoke, "Nothing I'd like more. But I'm off to New York next week." Lawrence tried to hide his disappointment when they said goodbye at the station. He felt more alone than he had ever done before, and as he walked on through the rainy streets his heart ached for that other time that Mary had re-kindled in him.

He knew now, in his heart that she could only ever be a friend, a special friend who he loved in childhood, like a sister. He sighed deeply as he opened the door of his empty bed-sit.

Echoes of Another Time

Lawrence lay rigid and motionless in the hospital coronary unit, his bright fearful eyes staring at the ceiling. The surgery was due to begin in the morning and his terror of it was growing with every passing minute. He had managed a brave face earlier when Maureen and his daughters visited him, but now alone the terror he had been trying to control all day took over his whole being.
The suddenness of his heart attack and the urgent need for by-pass surgery had shattered his world like the sudden breaking of glass.
He had built up a business empire in less than twenty-five years through sheer hard work. He knew now that he had worked too hard, spent too many hours away from home and had too little time for his family. Looking back, he also knew only too well that he had missed almost all of his children's growing years. They had all the things that money could buy, but he envied the closeness they shared with Maureen.
As his fears mounted a voice he recognised penetrated his terror filled thoughts, "Had to see for myself that it was really you. You're not doing too well eh? Come on Lawrence. It's me." Leaning over him she shook his shoulders gently. It's Mary from home. I'm a nurse here and when I saw your name on the notes - well here I am. Look I know you're not in the mood for small talk, so I'll talk shop. You know that this is routine nowadays and

that you'll recover fine." He made no reply and she could see by his fearful expression that she wasn't getting through to him.

"I'll go and get you written up for something to relax you. Back in a jiffy."

He was only vaguely aware of the injection she gave him and the hand that held his. It was her soft reassuring voice from other times long ago that penetrated his fearful, confused thoughts. Slowly the fear began to subside and he was able to look at her for the first time. "I'm sorry. Just felt like a terrified child for a while. I can't believe it's you. Must be divine intervention or something."

"Nothing Divine about me Lawrence. Just doing night duty, to keep the wolf from the door. But I'm glad I was here tonight for you."

"Not half as glad as me. Bet you think I'm an oul' coward."

She smiled and shook her head. "I'd never think that about you Lawrence. It happens to most. But, you'll be grand."

"When I get over this I'm going to build a house back home and get somebody else to take over the company for me."

"That's the spirit," she said, with a smile.

Now tell me about you," he asked,

"Are you married? Any family?"

"I'm separated and that's too long a story for now. I have two kids almost grown and I'm content enough under the circumstances. I haven't been home in ages."

"How come?"

"My mother's gone now - nobody to welcome me anymore. And the finances are a bit tight. But seeing you again, has made me long to escape back to that innocent time of childhood." Tomorrow when all's over I'll tell you a story about Pat and his aeroplane." He smiled, he could feel himself relax as sleep, blessed sleep stole over him. Forcing his eyes open again he said, "I've just decided - we're having a school reunion, the expense will be on me." Mary watched as a tear slowly trickled down his cheek. Then he said, "I can't wait to hear another heroic Pat story. In fact I'm determined to hear it."

Boots for Christmas

The black Ford travelled slowly through the small town, bustling with early Christmas shoppers, then turned left towards the district hospital. The woman stared fearfully ahead into the sleety rain of the laden November afternoon in 1955. Then she glanced at the fretful small child seated on her knee and gave her a smile of reassurance as she tucked the blanket around her small feverish body. As they turned in the hospital gates she said, "I want to go back home. The pain's better now."

"That's good Hanna. But it's only because of the injection the doctor gave you pet. They will help you to get better in the hospital."

As the stark greyness of the hospital came closer, Hanna's fear of the unknown grew into a terror that totally consumed her. "It's a pity that the new hospital isn't finished," Michael remarked from the driver's seat, glancing at the new building a short distance away.

The big door opened and from the shadowy depths beyond the figure of a nurse emerged; the stiff white cap fanned out around the tips of her shoulders, giving her a ghostly appearance.

"The doctor will be here soon," she said, as Hanna was carried into a long ward with beds lining the sides, and a blazing turf fire glowing at the far end. Taking her from her mother's arms, she laid her in a bed between stiff white sheets. Looking down at her small piquant face and the look of fear in her eyes, she said, "she looks very sick poor wee thing. But try not to worry too much. The Doctor here is very good."

He came through the door at the end of the ward, a giant of a man who seemed to fill the space. The very sight of him sent shivers of terror through Hanna's body. She lay rigid while he examined and prodded the leg where the excruciating pain was now almost unbearable. He looked at the chart at the bottom of the bed, and read the referral letter again with a puzzled frown on his face. Beckoning her mother a short distance from the bed, Hannah listened careful to what he said.

"It's not rheumatic fever. There's a serious infection in the ankle joint. Osteomylelitis; it's a disease of the bone. The infection is carried around the body via the blood stream. She is a very sick wee girl. We will start her on Penicillin. I will need to operate in the morning."

Hanna strained to listen to their conversation. The mention of 'operate,' sent alarm bells ringing in her head. The bright red scar that ran horizontally along her aunt's stomach sprang immediately into her mind.

"He is going to cut my leg open," she whispered in panic, while a short shower of tears ran down her face. He crossed the space between them in a couple of strides. "Don't be scared Hanna. We'll have your leg put to rights in no time. In the meantime I'll see that you get something for the pain." Then he smiled down at her; it was as if a sunset blazed behind his face and in that instant, some of her fears evaporated.

The following morning she found herself being

carried up two flights of stairs and through a door
to a brightly-lit room. Only eyes were visible and a
terror came over her as a suffocating mask was
placed over her mouth and nose, "breathe deeply.
Count to ten," a voice urged as she struggled in
panic to rid herself of the terrifying mask. Then
she felt her mind and body being dragged down;
she surrendered herself, for it seemed to offer relief
from the agony of the last few days. She could feel
the quick light beating of her heart. Now she was
being sucked down into a whirlpool, then swinging
up and up at an ever increasing speed, and as she
spun she seemed lifted out of herself and out of the
room - swept along in time and space...

Her recollections of the next day were hazy. She
found herself awakened back in the big ward with
the turf fire in the distance. Her mother sat beside
her holding her hand and wetting her lips, she slept
again and wakened to find her still there. This type
of in and out of consciousness seemed to go on
endlessly, until she finally awoke and found herself
lucid and aware of her situation. But her mother
was no longer beside her. She cried out in panic, "I
want my Mammy. I want to go home."
Through the blur of tears and panic, the kind face
of a patient nearby came into her vision. "It's all
right wee love. Your Mammy will be back soon.
She has gone home for a sleep. She's been here

for two days you know."

The next two days passed slowly and although her condition was improving, she pined for home, and the company of her siblings. Each visit from her mother brought relief, only to be replaced by despair when the time came to leave her again.

She awoke again to find the familiar face of her mother seated beside her once again. "I have brought you a book to read. It's a great story." Opening the book, she flicked through the pages absently. "There's no pictures," she said sulkily. "You don't need pictures. When you read the pictures come in your head. And they are by far the best pictures. Reading is a great form of escape. You can travel the world, and meet the most interesting people without having to travel at all. Aye, books are a great gift love. You try reading 'The Secret Garden' and see what I mean." When she had gone and her head ached from crying Hanna picked up the book reluctantly and slowly began to read; she read on and on, until the night-nurse extinguished the light above her bed. "Time to sleep Hanna. You'll get bad eyes reading so long." She finally fell asleep, with her thoughts on the haunting cries of the mystery child far away, in the dark old mansion somewhere in the Yorkshire moors.

The heavy footsteps of the doctor awoke her from a

heavy doze. "Well. How are we doing today?"

"I want to go home."

"You can't go home just yet Hanna. We have to wait for that leg of yours to heal. And the nurses tell me that you are not eating." Hanna stared back at him with tears beginning to sting the back of her eyes. Soon she began to sob uncontrollably. "My leg ... has ... has a hole in it. I've seen it."

"You're right. But that hole will soon disappear." He looked down at her, his face in a set of earnest wrinkles, then he asked, "do you want to go home for Christmas?" .

She nodded.

"Well then, you better start eating, and quick. Have you sent your letter to Santa?" She nodded again, the tears still trickling down her face.

"What did you ask him to bring you?"

"Boots. Boots with fur linings. And, a big doll," she added, as if the latter was an afterthought. Then the tears came again, filling her eyes and falling steadily down unto the stiff white sheet.

"Now what are you crying about?"

"The hole in my leg. I won't be able to wear the boots."

"If you eat and do what you're told, the leg will be healed in time for Santa." Then he walked away, leaving her alone with her self-pity. He returned a few minutes later with a sheet of white paper, and perched himself precariously at the end of her bed.

Taking a pen from his pocket, he began making quick strokes, up and down the paper. Reaching up to the locker, he removed a red crayon. "All right if I borrow this?" He asked, without glancing at her. When he had finished he propped the piece of paper up on her locker. "That's your boots. Now, I want you to imagine yourself wearing these on Christmas day. If you want it to happen enough, it will. Now no more tears." She could not resist his friendliness and enthusiasm, and she smiled up at him. He walked away humming 'jingle bells'. When the echo of his footsteps faded away, she stared intently at the red boots that he had drawn, then her gaze moved to the window. A light snow flurry fell gently against the panes, and slid silently down. As she watched, her feet ran across the fresh snow clad in the new red boots.

A Police Record

"**I**'d know that laugh anywhere," a voice from behind sounded amongst the hub of noise at the school reunion. Turning around I saw Joe grinning at me from a great height.

Finding a quiet corner we told each other about the thirty years since we last met. "And … I have only the one police record. The one I got curtsy of Minnie when I was ten," he ended. Suddenly

Minnie's memory was as clear as if the intervening thirty years were as the twinkling of an eye.

She entered the kitchen like a thunder cloud; a tall plump woman with a flat back and long feet that pointed out sideways when she walked.

"Evening Minnie. You're a bit of a stranger. Sit yourself down."

"It's not a social call. I've got a complaint."

From our position on the sofa we listened and watched with sinking spirits. In our minds we were back on the road from school, when Mick suggested saying 'hello Minnie the smithy' as she passed on her bike. Now, looking at the formidable figure standing in front of the kitchen stove, it suddenly didn't seem such a good idea.

Looking across to where we sat, she began again. "I was insulted on my way home today." The eyes that looked in our direction were hostile, the round face agitated; the plump hands united in front of her in a tight grasp.

"Sit down and take the weight of your legs first," Robert said, plumping up the cushion on the chair next to him. She seemed to relax a little as she sat on the chair.

"Now tell me about the insult and where we come into things."

Clearing her throat she began. "Well, I was on my way home from delivering an important message today. As I was passing the scholars on their way from school they shouted, 'Hello Minnie the smithy.' "Bold brats, that's what they are. Mind you I'm not saying your two were the worst. But I know the ring-leader and I'll see that every last one gets their just deserts."

Robert's face assumed a mildly shocked expression as he looked in our direction.

"Well what have you to say for yourselves? Did you insult Minnie?"

I could feel my face blaze as hostile eyes stared in my direction. "Well I … didn't know that … we were being insulting. Thought it was her name," I stammered lamely.

"You know right well it's not my name," Minnie screeched.

"Get up to your feet and apologise. Both of you," Robert ordered.

Getting up we stood demurely in front of Minnie. Her large face was red with anger, her lips twitching at the corners as she stared up at us without blinking.

"We're sorry. We won't do it again."

Turning her gaze to John, she said, "I want to hear that from both of you."

"I'm sorry too." John said, quietly.

"Speak up - I didn't hear that."

"I said I'm sorry," he repeated.

"Well then I'll have to accept your apology I

suppose," she said, grudgingly with a wave of dismissal.

Seated back on the sofa we wondered how we would make our escape to warn the others of her impending arrival. She continued to glare in our direction at ten second intervals between complaints of the unmannerly youth of the day. There was no escape.

We watched our mother take a tray of buns from the oven. As the delicious smell wafted Minnie's way her nose twitched.

Later she was presented with a plate full of the buns and a cup of tea - she protested. "Oh, you shouldn't have bothered making tea for me. I had tea just before I left. Mind you my appetite wasn't so good after all the upset with the scholars," she added, glowering menacingly in our direction once more.

She devoured the buns one by one, licking the butter periodically from the corners of her mouth. "Some more?" mother offered presenting her with another plate. "No, God love you no. I'm fit to burst. Well, maybe just one more," she said, reaching for another one.

"You could manage two," mother coaxed, edging the plate closer.

When at last she finished eating and drinking the endless cups of strong tea her mood had taken a turn for the better.

Robert lit his pipe. "Your grandfather was a great blacksmith. Some of his handy-work is still in evidence around here. Aye, you must be proud of his memory."

"Aye," she said, her voice hoarse and ragged. "He was good at his work."

As the discussion about her grandfather continued the earlier hostility seemed to seep away and we began to relax. But it was short lived. Getting to her feet she dusted the crumbs from her lap, then glowering in our direction she said,

"I must be going. I promised myself I'd get to all the parents of those brats tonight."

We waited impatiently as our parents saw her to the door and bid her goodnight. From the hallway we heard Robert say, "Poor woman. If she's depending on the friends she made during her lifetime to come to her wake, it could be held in a phone box."

Waiting until Robert was seated again John began. "Daddy can I go down and warn Joe? His father will kill him if she tells," he pleaded.

With a sigh, he said, "Go on then. But let this be a lesson to all of you. See all the bother you caused with your stupidity?"

We were out through the door as he spoke, running at speed through the fields in a desperate effort to reach Joe's house ahead of her.

Beckoning Joe outside, we had just finished telling about Minnie's threats when we saw the light from her bicycle coming up the lane. A minute later she was banging on the kitchen door.

Joe ushered us to safety behind the garden wall where we could watch unobserved.

Joe's wee sister came to the door and we heard her say in a loud voice, "Tell your father I want to speak to him. Tell him Miss Minnie Moran wants to speak to him."

"Miss Minnie," Joe whispered mockingly. "An' my father's in the worst of humour too. Been cutting corn all day."

After what seemed an age Joe's father came to the door. "Oh, it's you. The 'Miss' bit threw me."

"I have a serious complaint to make about your son. Am I to come in or do we have this out on the doorstep?" she asked, in a high pitched tone.

"The doorstep will do if this is your attitude," John retorted angrily.

"He insulted me today. I was passing by minding my own business when the scholars shouted at me. 'Hello Minnie the smithy,' they chanted. Aye, an' your son was the ringleader."

There was a period of silence in which we could hear our hearts beating before Joe's father replied. "If you didn't throw a tantrum like you're doing right now, they wouldn't bother you."

"I demand an apology from him right now. I'm not leaving 'till I get it. If not, I'm going to make

my complaint in the Garda barracks."
"They'd only laugh at you. And anyway, what's wrong with being called the smithy? Your grandfather was a blacksmith - wasn't he?"
 "If this is your attitude to a serious complaint like mine I'll get a better hearing from the Sergeant."
"Well away you go then. I have better things to do than stand here arguing with you." With that he walked back into the house.

Joe wasn't to get off the hook so easily. The following evening, on his way home from school the Sergeant stood waiting for him at the end of the lane, his silver buttons gleaming in the yellow evening light.
He told him he would let him off with a warning this time. "You should know that Minnie always demands satisfaction one way or another," he commented, as he scribbled in his notebook. "Now you have a police record. Hope that will teach you when you cross Minnie's path again."

The Funeral

Hanna parked her car in the church car-park and headed towards the gate that led to the graveyard. She found graveyards peaceful, reflective places, places where she could reflect life and death, past and present, bygone generations and those whom she remembered from her own time.

Sitting down on a tree trunk, Hanna smiled to herself at the thought of what her other half would say when she told him she had visited another graveyard, "Morbid occupation if you ask me," he always retorted.

Then looking at the inscription on the headstone beside her, her heartbeat quickened. 'IN LOVING MEMORY OF MAUREEN LOUGHLIN' it read. Although she hadn't known Maureen in life, she felt that she knew her in death and now she recalled the valuable lesson she had learned because of Maureen Loughlin's passing. Suddenly, she was a child again seated under the old sycamore tree in the school-yard.

The school bell rang out just ten minutes into playtime on a warm autumn afternoon. Reluctant feet shuffled towards the school entrance with bewildered expressions. Standing near the doorway, the schoolmaster cleared his throat.

"A funeral will pass the school in a few minutes time," he began, "and I want you all to stand facing the gate. And if you move a muscle, I'll be watching."

A few minutes later the funeral procession reached the school gates. Two black horses drew the hearse, their hooves moving almost silently through the fallen leaves. Dozens of mourners shuffled behind on foot, their voices barely above a whisper, and behind them two black motor cars carrying the next of kin, their pale faces staring straight ahead as the cars moved slowly past.

When the entire procession had passed, Hanna and Mary walked slowly towards the sycamore tree and sat down silently underneath it. They could hear the drowsy drone of a big velvet bumble-bee mingling with the other childrens' voices as play was resumed. Mary stared straight ahead before she spoke. "I went with my mother to sit with old Minnie the night before she died. They said she wouldn't last long because she had the death rattle in her throat." Hanna visibly shuddered. "It's horrible to die. But I suppose she's in heaven by now. What a pity we couldn't do it without dying." "Do what without dying?" Mary asked, with a puzzled frown.

"Go to heaven."

"You say the silliest things sometimes," Mary said, trying to strike a note of disinterested dignity. "Minnie used to make me sugar sandwiches and she always had sweets for me on a Friday evening."

"But she must be in heaven if she was good to everybody, and you'll see her there some day when you die," Hanna said, reassuringly.

Mary looked at her friend and smiled. Then a deep frown crossed her face. "You are a Protestant and I'm a Catholic - right? What if God sends us to separate heavens because we go to different churches?"

Hanna's face clouded as she gave this vexed

question serious consideration. There was a poignant silence for a minute or so before Hanna spoke again. "God is supposed to know everything right?"

"Well," she continued, "If he knows everything - then he knows that you and me are best friends. So he wouldn't put us in separate heavens."

Mary nodded. Then a broad smile lit up her face. "You're right. We'll go and play before the bell goes."

To go at Christmas

Hanna was pinning the last paper chain to the ceiling when she heard the front door open. Mary O' Gormon stood blinking in the sudden brightness and then slumped down panting in the nearest chair. "It's the wind. It fair takes your breath away. Where's your mother?"

"Stuffing the goose."

"Go and tell her I'm here ... there's a good girl,"

she added.

When her mother appeared wiping her hands on her apron, Mary got to her feet. "I've just heard that Thomas McGovern was found dead in his bed this morning. Aye, and him complaining away about the world and his wife as usual, at bedtime. It just goes to show you, you never know your day or your hour."

Thomas lived in a grey stone house at the foot of the whin hill with his niece Margaret and two cross dogs. He was a small man, who walked very erect, taking extraordinarily long steps as though he wanted to convince the world and himself that he was really a big man. It was the only house in the townland out of bounds to children. If they ventured anywhere near his abode, he shouted threats at them. This combined with the dogs vicious barking and bearing of teeth kept them all well away. He had spent most of his life in America, and his retirement complaining about the lack of local amenities, the weather, incompetence, and just about anything, each new day brought to his notice. Although Hanna had disliked him in life, she felt a little sad about his passing.

'Christmas belongs with warmth, with love, with good cheer, with feasting, with presents; not with dying,' she thought mournfully.

"I better go down and give Margaret a hand," her mother's voice broke into her thoughts.

"Aye, she had the patience of a saint with him.
God be good to him; but he was a crabbit wee man.
Tell her I'll be down the morrow," Mary said,
getting to her feet.
When she had gone, her mother put on her coat and
got the torch. "Will you come with me?" she asked
Hanna, "I hate going up on my own."

 Hanna wished that they were going somewhere
else other than the house of a dead man, as they
made their way down the lane. The air was crisp
and the full moon just rising above the horizon,
created Christmas magic in her head. As they
neared the remote house the 'chug, chug, chug,' of
the generator shattered the magic of the still, frosty
night. Thomas had found fault with the ESB, and
decided to produce his own. "God only knows
how he stood that racket," her mother commented,
as they reached the house.

Dressed in black, his niece Margaret met them at
the door. "He got a quick call," she said, as they
shook hands and followed her into the narrow hall.
Margaret pointed to a door at the right. "He's in
there," she said. "There's no one in there yet; it's
still a bit early."
Hanna followed them into the glum parlour, full of
rows of brown chairs. At the far end, was the

brown coffin; to Hanna it seemed huge, a box fit for a giant. She advanced upon it slowly behind her mother, and saw Thomas in death. He seemed diminutive, lost in the recesses of his mighty container. His small hands were folded across his chest, and over his coffin a large silver crucifix was suspended. Someone had fixed a spotlight, so that it played full on the crucifix, and high above Thomas's final, alien smile, the white light glittered and danced.

"Stay here a minute. I need to go and have a word with Margaret," her mother said, leaving her alone. Suddenly, from somewhere on the right, there came a 'Sssst!' She jumped. In a corner darker than the rest of the room she saw the small puckered face of old Joan, his nearest neighbour, peering out at her. "Did I scare you pet?" she said with delight. She raised herself to a half-standing posture and gazed critically at the coffin. "I hear he bought the coffin years ago. Far too big for him. Doesn't he look well? Aye and that wee smile on his face too. But, God be good to him .... he didn't waste many smiles when he was living. That's for sure." Because of her deafness, Joan didn't hear his niece, and other relations come into the room. Hanna nudged her arm, but to no avail. "Aye, and him to be buried on Christmas Eve too. He was thran when he was living; and he took a thran day to die."

Hazel McIntyre

Hazel McIntyre was born on a farm in the Innishowen pensinula of Co. Donegal in Ireland. After leaving school she moved to London where she became a nurse, before marrying husband Charles.
They later moved back to Ireland, in the 1970's where they now live with their three children.

Her first book 'Iron Wheels on Rocky Lanes' which vividly recalled her Donegal childhood was first published in 1994 to an outstanding ovation from the critics. Her first work of fiction 'For Love of Mary Kate' was published in 1996 and told the powerful and compelling tale of three generations of women in 1920's rural Ireland. It was hailed by newspaper critics as 'the first of many fine novels from this emerging Donegal writer.' 'For Love of Mary Kate' was chosen by Woman's Way magazine for their Millennium edition.

Hazel McIntyre's novel 'Lament In The Wind' was launched in October 1999. Beginning in the present, the carefully researched work of fiction set against the background of famine Ireland, tells the compelling story of Cassie O' Connor. It has already been described 'as a story that will live long in the memory of the reader.'
'Lament in the wind' is not only Hazel McIntyre's tribute to the victims of The Great Hunger, but is also a tribute to the courage and dignity of the human spirit.

In addition to her role as writer, housewife and mother Hazel McIntyre runs creative writing classes, gives talks to womens' groups, support groups and also radio and television interviews in Ireland, the USA and Canada